BMW i3 Concept

We believe that driving responsibly shouldn't mean you have to compromise on enjoyment. That's why we've created incredibly efficient and dynamic electric cars, from the Megacity Vehicle BMW i3 Concept to the exhilarating sports car BMW i8 Concept. Both offer progressive designs and shapes created out of futuristic lightweight carbon fibre. We've combined premium interior design with natural and sustainable materials. Intelligent applications and services will connect you to your city faster, more easily and more conveniently than ever before. These are just a few of the ways BMW i is creating a new world of visionary mobility.

BMW i. BORN ELECTRIC.   **bmw-i.co.uk**

official partner to
London 2012

LIVE FOR GREATNESS

EVERY ROLEX IS MADE FOR GREATNESS. SINCE 1971, THE EXPLORER II
HAS ACCOMPANIED EXPEDITIONS AROUND THE WORLD. IT FEATURES A
24-HOUR HAND, WHICH IS INVALUABLE TO SPELEOLOGISTS AND POLAR
EXPLORERS AS IT ALLOWS THEM TO DISTINGUISH DAY FROM NIGHT. THE
LATEST EXPLORER II FEATURES A 42 MM CASE AND IS THE IDEAL INSTRUMENT
TO HELP TODAY'S EXPEDITIONS PUSH THE BOUNDARIES EVEN FURTHER.

THE EXPLORER II

Photographed by Tim Laman

WILDLIFE AS CANON SEES IT

Its eyes are matched by its appetite. The western tarsier has huge eyes—a single eyeball is larger than its brain—and consumes a prodigious one-tenth of its body weight each night. The nocturnal hunter uses sound to locate large insects, arachnids or small animals and then pounces. Highly adapted for leaping, it is capable of covering a distance equal to some 40 times its own head and body length in a single bound. It can also turn its head 180 degrees, like an owl. But there is danger no matter which way it turns, as the forest falls due to logging and conversion to oil palm plantations.

As we see it, we can help make the world a better place. Raising awareness of endangered species is just one of the ways we at Canon are taking action—for the good of the planet we call home. Visit **canon.com/environment** to learn more.

Canon

VOL. 220 · NO. 5
NOVEMBER 2011

NATIONAL GEOGRAPHIC

It appears he was tranquilly digesting his meal, unaware of the danger he was in.
page 132

62

FEATURES

38 **Mysterious Hoard**
An English field has yielded
3,500 gold, silver, and garnet
objects. Who buried them?
By Caroline Alexander
Photographs by Robert Clark
Art by Daniel Dociu

62 **Life With Reindeer**
ATVs and snowmobiles help
Scandinavia's Sami keep
their herder heritage alive.
By Jessica Benko
Photographs by Erika Larsen

82 **Rift in Paradise**
Africa's Albertine Rift is rich
in resources, animals—and
crushingly violent conflicts.
By Robert Draper
Photographs by Pascal Maitre
and Joel Sartore

118 **Iceman Unfrozen**
To find out how Europe's
5,300-year-old mummy died,
scientists had to defrost him.
By Stephen S. Hall
Photographs by Robert Clark

134 **Boundless Rivers**
A little-known law safeguards
hundreds of America's wild
and scenic waterways.
By Joel K. Bourne, Jr.
Photographs by Michael Melford

Special Poster:
Africa's Rift Valley/
Great Lakes

On the Cover
Our artist depicted gold and silver
artifacts from the Staffordshire
Hoard in his painting of war garb.
Art by Daniel Dociu

DEPARTMENTS

Editor's Note
Letters
National Geographic on TV

VISIONS

Your Shot
Photo Journal

NOW

- **Spider Powers**
- **Retiring Space Shuttles**
- **Cranberry Clout**
- **Global Gas Prices**
- **Sensitive Seal Whiskers**
- **Oldest Koi**

NEXT

- **Umbrella Technology**
- **The 100-Year-Old Baby**
- **3-D Mummy**
- **The Code of Zebras**

NG Connect
The Moment
Flashback

FOR SUBSCRIPTIONS, GIFT MEMBERSHIPS,
OR CHANGES OF ADDRESS, CONTACT CUSTOMER
SERVICE AT *NGMSERVICE.COM* OR CALL
1-800-NGS-LINE (647-5463). OUTSIDE THE U.S.
AND CANADA PLEASE CALL +1-813-979-6845.

 Please recycle.

The Paradox of Geography

What began as an attempt to do my job in Africa's Albertine Rift still haunts me. A lovely young woman carrying firewood on her back was walking through lush forest. My guide, a local schoolteacher, asked the woman if I could take her picture. She readily agreed. Afterward I asked if it was appropriate to reward her graciousness. As I gave her a modest amount of money to make her life a little easier, a man swinging a machete burst out of the forest, screaming that he was her husband. In a drunken rage, he demanded more cash and threatened us. As we began to drive off, I glanced at the rearview mirror and saw the man beating her. I stopped and ran toward the stricken woman, but my guide pulled me back. He knew the man, he said. The situation could become more violent if I intervened. The man saw us and stopped his assault. They both waved me on. Reluctantly, I returned to my car, furious at the man and with myself, because I felt responsible for what had happened.

The Rift is a landscape shaped by violence.

Mai-Mai Kifuafua militia troops control Rift territory in the Democratic Republic of the Congo. They believe greenery offers magical protection.

Five years later, in 1994, that region was the scene of more violence: the mass murder known as the Rwandan genocide.

The Albertine Rift, as writer Robert Draper and photographers Pascal Maitre and Joel Sartore show us in this month's story, is a landscape shaped by violence—the convulsions of plate tectonics produced its beautiful lakes, savannas, and mountains. But the overlay of human violence on its geography is unremittingly ugly. The Rift is a malignant tangle of human need and suffering. For millennia, people have crowded into the region, attracted by its fertile land and minerals. "The paradox," Draper says, "is that its very richness has led to scarcity," and in the story you will read why. This dilemma provokes the unshakable worry: Is there enough for everyone? That's the pervading question in this seventh story in our Seven Billion series on world population.

PHOTO: PASCAL MAITRE

● *Privacy with a touch of class*

Royal First Class

re-flight, my privacy begins with an escort service through the dedicated
heck-in and access to premium lounges. In-flight, it's the luxury of travelling in
fully reclining spacious seat. I'm soothed into a state of serenity by world-class
ntertainment while indulging in the pre-ordered menu with my own wine list.
oyal First gives me privacy with a touch of class every time I fly THAI.

THAI
Smooth as silk

ew Royal First Class seats available on A340-600
nd selected B747-400 aircraft on selected routes.

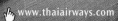

Get closer to nature in Thailand

Walking Thailand's Den Ya Khat trail brings you face-to-face with a timeless panorama: the rising sun shimmering over the mist-covered canopy of a verdant forest stretching as far as the eye can see. The view is as breathtaking as it is unexpected—this is the true beauty of Thailand.

Few places on Earth can boast such natural beauty, from cloud-covered mountains through rich emerald forests to stunning sandy beaches. And now Thailand wants its visitors to get even closer to nature.

The Tourism Authority of Thailand (TAT) is encouraging visitors to embrace the nature of Thailand by exploring this amazing country along its less trodden paths of hills, forests, and rivers—experiencing the true essence of Thailand.

This philosophy, that seeks to connect person with place through nature, goes hand-in-hand with a nascent and sincere commitment to sustainable eco-tourism. TAT's "Seven Green Concepts" lay down a framework that encourages a more responsible approach to tourism rooted in a greater appreciation of Thailand's natural beauty.

It's a change in which the tourists themselves play a significant role. Visiting eco-destinations encourages and underpins Thailand's emergent green efforts. From walking through the botanist's paradise of Doi Phu Kha to cycling around the Si Satchanalai UNESCO World Heritage site or rafting down the spectacular Khek River, these off-the-beaten-track holidays let you reach out and touch nature—while helping to preserve it. And in so doing, as at Den Ya Khat, we can all discover the true beauty of Thailand.

THE MOST AMAZING SHOW ON EARTH

The Lo Re waterfall Tak

Food Ark

As an old poultry raiser, I was thrilled to see pages 112-13 of the July issue actually devoted to uncommon chickens. I raised Golden Laced Wyandotte bantams for about 40 years. My birds supposedly were some of the best in the Midwest, if not in the entire country. I even had poultry judges tell me what great birds they were. But did I ever get Best of Breed when I exhibited them? Nope. The judges either sought out a White Wyandotte or a Black Wyandotte

▶ for that honor. The darn poultry judges are responsible for driving many fine breeds out of existence.

D. DAVID DE LAND
Bellevue, Nebraska

I regularly travel across much of America's breadbasket states on a motorcycle that gets 50 to 75 miles a gallon. I have noticed more and more corn being grown in fields once planted with other edible crops. "Big yields," say the farmers when I inquire, but the corn feeds nothing but SUVs, fuel-consuming sedans, and trucks. Fewer kernels are ever eaten. Rather the corn is turned into grain alcohol for internal combustion engines. There is not a food crisis; there's a stupidity crisis, based on greed and glut. Want to feed a planet—or feed SUVs that get 15 miles a gallon in town? We Americans have it so good. Consume, consume, consume… Conserve? Not a chance. Not yet!

J. AARON CUNDALL
Helena, Montana

When poor people around the world continue to have 10 to 15 kids when they can't afford one, there will never be a solution to the problem of feeding this planet. Do you think a farmer in Latin America or Africa trying to feed his dozen kids is going to care if climate change kills off the last polar bear? The planet will probably be around for a while. I doubt that people will. But hey, keep storing those special seeds. They will solve everything.

TOM R. KOVACH
Nevis, Minnesota

Saving seeds is a good way to preserve local varieties of crops while scientists and farmers work to reintroduce them to their natural habitats. But there is no way to store livestock in the same fashion. Livestock's genetic diversity is declining more slowly than crops', but it is still in decline. This should be cause for as much concern as with crops.

PATRICK TESSMER
Byron Center, Michigan

Corrections and Clarifications
AUGUST 2011 Our international edition's cover was a composite image: The robot should have been credited to Robert Clark, the background to Getty Images.

FEEDBACK *This graphic shows reader responses for articles that received ten or more letters.*

■ Positive
Neutral
■ Negative

"The water's too hot for the **polar bears** and too cold for the **manatees**?"

"It's frustrating when you can't find a dead body. What a royal pain!"

It's encouraging to see this issue being highlighted.

Cleopatra was ugly.

Type sizes are too small.

Cover   Letters   Baghdad After the Storm   On Thin Ice   Middle East Youth   NOW, NEXT   The Search for Cleopatra   Food Ark

 EMAIL ngsforum@ngm.com **TWITTER** @NatGeoSociety **WRITE** National Geographic Magazine, PO Box 98199, Washington, DC 20090-8199. Include name, address, and daytime telephone. Letters may be edited for clarity and length.

GRAPHIC: LAWSON PARKER, NGM STAFF

BRING

TO

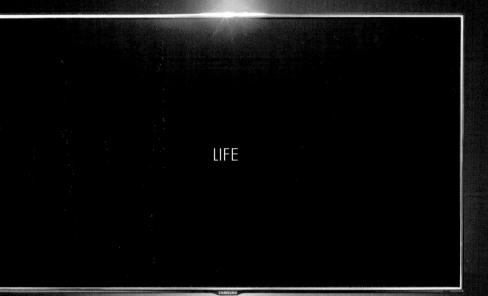

LIFE

INFINITE

POSSIBILITIES

Samsung SMART TV Join in.

Immerse yourself in incredible content with Samsung Smart TV.
Samsung Smart TV brings it all together.

I was struck by the parallels between the global food supply and a person's investment portfolio. To achieve consistently solid returns, virtually all investment managers agree on principles of diversification to protect against losses. And past performance is not a guarantee of future returns. Yet in addressing the goal of a consistent world food supply, the approach of big agriculture has been one of little diversity and total reliance on what has been successful most recently in a select group of regions. We saw what happened in the investment world when people put their entire portfolios into dot-coms or real estate. Should we expect it to be any different with agriculture?

JOE MILLER
Cayucos, California

Cremation was a standard Roman way to dispose of bodies. It was suitable for nobles.

I'm delighted to see "Food Ark" highlighting the urgent need to protect and preserve our precious crop biodiversity. However, I must take exception to the photos on page 123 and the caption indicating that these are all potatoes. Five of the tubers shown are the root crop oca (*Oxalis tuberosa,* not even the same genus as potatoes, *Solanum tuberosum).* These vividly colored, nutty-sweet tubers are prominent in Andean agriculture, but they are most definitely not potatoes.

CAROL GOLAND
Executive Director
Ohio Ecological Food
& Farm Association
Columbus, Ohio

The images on page 123 were meant to depict the great diversity of South American tubers. It's true that some shown are ocas and others are potatoes; what's similar is that they are both tubers, and are harvested and eaten in the same way. We used the more familiar term "potato" in the generic sense even though they are different plants.

In "How to Feed a Growing Planet" a claim is made that soybeans provide up to 15 times more protein per acre than land set aside for meat production. This argument overlooks some important facts. There are large tracts of land on this planet that are suitable for grazing but quite useless for growing crops. Also, while many people are able to live comfortably on a vegetarian diet, there is a sizable proportion who, for physiological reasons, cannot. Implications to the effect that all proteins are nutritionally similar serve no good purpose. Certainly there is a place for the soybean in today's world, but possibly not as a substantial element in some human diets.

JOHN WATSON
Bathurst, Australia

The Search for Cleopatra

I submit that Kathleen Martinez and the other searchers for Cleopatra's tomb are barking up the wrong tree. Isn't it possible that Cleopatra and Mark Antony were not buried but rather cremated? Cremation was a standard Roman way to dispose of bodies. It was suitable for nobles. Furthermore, it was common for those in power to cremate their rivals in order to avoid creation of shrines by sympathizers of the dead.

ROBERT F. FOX
San Antonio, Texas

I thoroughly enjoyed reading the article on Cleopatra. But I believe that it gave far too much credit to Octavian. We are referring to a man who led a war, divided and conquered one of the greatest empires of history, and after these "victories," murdered his own stepbrother, who was the more rightful heir to Julius Caesar. After all, Octavian was only the nephew (and adoptive son) of Julius Caesar, while Caesarion was the blood son of Julius Caesar and Cleopatra. Do we really believe that Octavian would be honorable enough to respect and carry out the burial wishes of Mark Antony and Cleopatra? I believe the more likely scenario is that once Alexandria was conquered, Octavian ordered their bodies to be simply thrown into the latrine. This would certainly explain why nobody ever found anything.

SHARON ULAM
Riverside, California

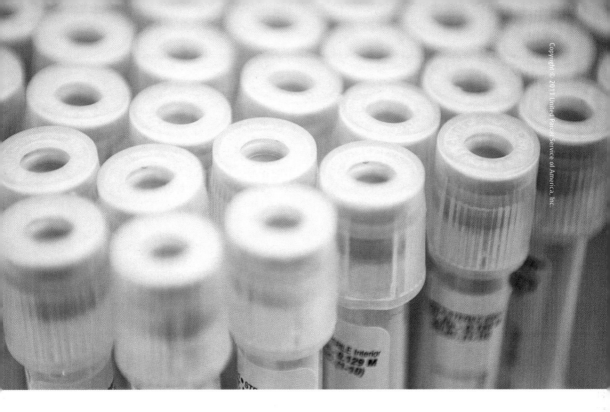

THE LOGISTICS OF AN ANTI-DOPING PROGRAMME.

These days, every high-level competitive event has to worry about performance-enhancing drugs. The Olympic Games are no exception. As the Official Logistics Supporter of London 2012, UPS will be transporting the biological samples of the athletes for testing.

CRITICAL SHIPMENTS

These biological samples, it should be noted, are very delicate. They will have to be shipped safely and handled with care. Because of our logistical experience, UPS was given the job of transporting these critical vials and sample bottles.

RIGHT TIME, RIGHT CONDITION

UPS will make sure the samples get to the labs for analysis while they are still viable. UPS technology will also provide up-to-the-minute visibility at key stages along the way. (This same UPS technology can make your supply chain more visible and therefore your company more responsive.)

PARTNERSHIPS

UPS is working closely with the London 2012 organisers. But we partner with all businesses to provide the best service. We have tremendous depth of experience working with pharmaceutical and medical device companies. See how we can help you.

For the details, go to
ups.com/london2012

WE ♥ LOGISTICS™

official supporter

LETTERS

Your fascinating account of the search for Cleopatra's tomb began with the statement that she was the "world's first celebrity." If that phrase has any meaning at all, it surely describes not Cleopatra but the man who conquered Egypt— Alexander the Great. As he went to war with Persia, Alexander brought along historians to write of his exploits, painters to paint them, and sculptors to sculpt them. He was unlike modern celebrities, who often do nothing to merit their fame. Alexander didn't just wage war, he wanted to make sure everyone knew about it. Cleopatra learned his lesson well, but it was more than three centuries in the making.

LEO BRAUDY
Los Angeles, California

Alexander didn't just wage war, he wanted to make sure everyone knew about it.

I disagree with the characterization of Cleopatra as the world's first celebrity, notwithstanding that "five ballets, 45 operas, and 77 plays," and at least seven movies are about her. The universally recognized criterion for celebrity is that a diner in the borough of Queens, New York, is named after the person. Thus, I note the Helen of Troy diner I once visited in the aforementioned Queens.

JOSEPH F. KRUPSKY
Easton, Pennsylvania

I enjoyed your article on Cleopatra; however, I was floored that you got through it without a single reference to global warming, since it appears on every other page of every issue. Surely you could have attributed the sunken city of old Alexandria to it.

JIM MILLER
Mountville, South Carolina

The detailed graphic of Cleopatra's Alexandria showing intense coastal development is starkly reminiscent of today's coastal Florida, or indeed my home in southeast Queensland, Australia—even to the point of having early development of canals. If climate scientists are correct, Alexandria's ultimate fate will also befall these areas as sea levels rise and super-storms become more common. This is a clear illustration of how little we have learned in 2,000 years.

LYNDON DEVANTIER
Noosaville, Australia

Baghdad After the Storm

Thank you for the story about Baghdad. It is amazing how with all the destruction and mayhem of war, the people of Baghdad keep on going and building their future. This is something lots of Westerners forget: Learn to treasure life and the opportunities it brings to you. Keep kindness, and do not surrender under any circumstances. You are the one who can change it and build it up.

VLADIMIR BOGAK
San Francisco, California

Not Too Late for Polar Bears

It is obvious that polar bears need sea ice to survive, but why not attempt a temporary solution? Large floating white plastic islands of various sizes could be manufactured and chained to the seafloor in appropriate locations. This would not only give wildlife a place to rest and feed but also be a great use for a great deal of recycled plastic.

WILLIAM T. MOULTON
Port St. Lucie, Florida

Explorers Journal

Regarding the photograph on page 11: Improvised snow goggles have been used in Europe for over a century, long before we ever heard of duct tape. Cardboard with a cross cut into it can be used together with string. This produced a variable aperture to suit varying light conditions. And you could see your boots! Our group from the United Kingdom used a humble cornflakes packet and bits of tent guyline on an impromptu ascent of Mont Blanc in 1967.

BOB WILSON
Baho, France

Visions of Earth

Am I the only one to notice the similarities between the spiraling moth flight time-lapse photo and the images I've seen elsewhere of the spiraling subatomic particles blasted out of photons at nearly light speed in superconducting supercolliders?

BILL CHANCELLOR
El Paso, Texas

Smarter business for a Smarter Planet:

Most boats are moved by propellers.
This one was moved by intelligence.

MarineMax®, the world's largest boat retailer, is using Cognos® business analytics software to make sure its boats aren't wasting away in showrooms, lowering net profits. By better aligning inventory decisions with customer demand, MarineMax reduced its forecasting cycle from 3 months to 3 weeks, cut costs by 48% and ultimately moved more boats. A smarter planet is built on smarter software, systems and services.

Let's build a smarter planet. **ibm.com**/insights/uk

Data visualisation of revenue
projections for monthly boat sales.

For just six glorious
hours, he didn't
feel endangered at all.
Our Cargo Team ensure
that we're equipped for
our most demanding
passengers. Orangutans
are on the edge of
extinction in the wild, and
this young male needed
highly-specialised care on
his recent journey home.
At least he was friendlier
than last year's leopard.

To Fly. To Serve.

oneworld

BRITISH AIRWAYS

Orangutans are one
of the smartest species
on the planet. But these
highly social, tool-using
primate brainboxes, face
a shrinking habitat and
dwindling population.

THIS MONTH

Swamp Men

At the north end of the Florida Everglades, on ancestral Seminole land, the Billie Swamp Safari park is home to alligators, rattlesnakes, red-tailed hawks, and more. Each year the 2,200-acre preserve attracts thousands of visitors who come to witness this unspoiled wilderness. Follow the park's staff in a new season of *Swamp Men* on Nat Geo WILD as they educate the public and maintain safety while honoring a traditional Seminole value: respect for the harmony of nature.

Jonathan Vazquez touches an alligator (above) as Gus Batista looks on in Billie Swamp Safari park.

NATIONAL GEOGRAPHIC CHANNEL

Secrets of the Lost Gold
Expedition Week is back with stories of discovery, including the find of a seventh-century treasure trove in England.

For listings go to **natgeotv.com** and **natgeowild.com**.

This is not the end of the journey, it's only the beginning.

Dunes of Liwa

Here, silence is serenity.

The quest for stillness is found amidst tranquillity.

And the vastness fills you with unforgettable peace.

Ever changing dunes. Unbridled wonder.

An endless horizon bathed in splendour.

Where every day dawns with the promise of a new beginning.

And you think you've seen it all?

Abu Dhabi. Travellers welcome.

Inspiring people to care about the planet

NATIONAL GEOGRAPHIC

The National Geographic Society is chartered in Washington, D.C., as a nonprofit scientific and educational organization "for the increase and diffusion of geographic knowledge."

NATIONAL GEOGRAPHIC MAGAZINE

EDITOR IN CHIEF **Chris Johns**
DEPUTY EDITOR Victoria Pope
CREATIVE DIRECTOR Bill Marr
EXECUTIVE EDITORS
Dennis R. Dimick *(Environment)*, Kurt Mutchler *(Photography)*, Jamie Shreeve *(Science)*
MANAGING EDITOR Lesley B. Rogers

TEXT **DEPUTY DIRECTOR:** Marc Silver. **STORY DEVELOPMENT EDITOR:** Barbara Paulsen
ARTICLES EDITOR: Oliver Payne
SENIOR EDITORS: Lynn Addison *(Features)*, Robert Kunzig *(Environment)*, Peter Miller *(Expeditions)*. EDITOR AT LARGE: Cathy Newman. FEATURES EDITORS: Glenn Oeland, Jane Vessels
EDITOR, MISSION PROJECTS: Hannah Bloch. ASSISTANT EDITOR: Amanda B. Fiegl
SENIOR WRITERS: Jennifer S. Holland, Tom O'Neill, A. R. Williams. WRITER: Peter Gwin
ADMINISTRATION: Imad Aoun; Katia Andreassi, Nicholas Mott
CONTRIBUTING WRITERS: Caroline Alexander, Don Belt, Joel K. Bourne, Jr., Robert Draper, Cynthia Gorney, Peter Hessler, Mark Jenkins, David Quammen
DEPARTMENTS DIRECTOR: Margaret G. Zackowitz
DEPUTY DIRECTOR: Luna Shyr. EDITOR: Jeremy Berlin. ADMINISTRATION: Catherine Zuckerman

PHOTOGRAPHY **DEPUTY DIRECTOR:** Ken Geiger
SENIOR EDITORS: Bill Douthitt *(Special Editions)*, Kathy Moran *(Natural History)*, Susan Welchman. EDITOR AT LARGE: Michael Nichols
SENIOR PHOTO EDITORS: Alice Gabriner, Kim Hubbard, Todd James, Elizabeth Krist, Sarah Leen, Sadie Quarrier. PHOTO EDITOR SPECIALIST: Deirdre Read. RESEARCH EDITOR: Mary McPeak
STAFF PHOTOGRAPHER: Mark Thiessen. STUDIO: Rebecca Hale. DIGITAL IMAGING: Edward Samuel, Evan Wilder. PHOTO ENGINEERING: Walter Boggs, David Mathews, Kenji Yamaguchi
RIGHTS MANAGER: Elizabeth Grady. ADMINISTRATION: Whitney Hall, Jenny Trucano; Sherry L. Brukbacher, Kate Napier, Elena Sheveiko

DESIGN/ART **DEPUTY CREATIVE DIRECTOR:** Kaitlin M. Yarnall. **DESIGN DIRECTOR:** David C. Whitmore
ART DIRECTOR: Juan Velasco. **MAPS DIRECTOR:** William E. McNulty
SENIOR DESIGN EDITORS: John Baxter, Elaine H. Bradley. DESIGN EDITOR: Oliver R. Uberti
SENIOR GRAPHICS EDITORS: Fernando G. Baptista, Martin Gamache, Virginia W. Mason, John Tomanio. SENIOR CARTOGRAPHY EDITOR: Gus Platis. ART RESEARCH EDITOR: Amanda Hobbs
GRAPHICS SPECIALISTS: Jerome N. Cookson, Lawson Parker, Maggie Smith
SENIOR DESIGNER: Betty Clayman-DeAtley. DESIGNERS: Sandi Owatverot-Nuzzo, Hannah Tak
ADMINISTRATION: Cinde Reichard; Michael Kritikos

COPY/RESEARCH **DEPUTY MANAGING EDITOR:** David Brindley
SENIOR COPY EDITOR: Mary Beth Oelkers-Keegan. COPY EDITORS: Kitry Krause, Cindy Leitner
DEPUTY RESEARCH DIRECTOR: Alice S. Jones. RESEARCH EDITORS: Heidi Schultz, Elizabeth Snodgrass, Christy Ullrich, Barbara L. Wyckoff. SENIOR RESEARCHERS: Karen C. Font, Nora Gallagher, David A. Lande, Nancie Majkowski, Taryn Salinas, Brad Scriber
PRODUCTION: Sandra Dane. ADMINISTRATION: Jacqueline Rowe

E-PUBLISHING **DIRECTOR:** Melissa Wiley. SENIOR VIDEO PRODUCER: Hans Weise. DESIGNER: Lindsay Powell
PRODUCTION SPECIALIST: Susan Park Lee. ADMINISTRATION: Trish Dorsey

NGM.COM SENIOR PRODUCERS: Paul Heltzel, John Kondis. ASSOCIATE PRODUCER: William Barr
SENIOR PHOTO EDITOR: Monica C. Corcoran. ART DIRECTOR: Shawn Greene

ADMINISTRATION Karen Dufort Sligh *(Asst. to the Editor in Chief)*, Valarie Cribb-Chapman *(Finance)*, Carol L. Dumont *(Scheduling)*; Nikisha Long; Alicia LaFrance
COMMUNICATIONS VICE PRESIDENTS: Beth Foster, Mary Jeanne Jacobsen; Barbara S. Moffet
IMAGE COLLECTION AND SALES VICE PRESIDENT: Maura A. Mulvihill; William D. Perry
LIBRARIES AND INFORMATION SERVICES DIRECTOR: Barbara Penfold Ferry; Renee Braden

PRODUCTION **SENIOR VICE PRESIDENT:** Phillip L. Schlosser
SERVICES IMAGING VICE PRESIDENT: Thomas J. Craig. GENERAL MANAGER: Bernard Quarrick; John Ballay, David J. Bulebush, Neal Edwards, James P. Fay, Arthur N. Hondros, Gregory Luce, Ann Marie Pelish, Stephen L. Robinson. PRINTING: Joseph M. Anderson. QUALITY DIRECTOR: Ronald E. Williamson; Clayton R. Burneston, Michael G. Lappin, William D. Reicherts
DISTRIBUTION DIRECTOR: Michael Swarr

INTERNATIONAL **EDITORIAL DIRECTOR:** Amy Kolczak
EDITIONS PHOTO AND DESIGN EDITOR: Darren Smith. PHOTOGRAPHIC LIAISON: Laura L. Ford
PRODUCTION: Angela Botzer. ADMINISTRATION: William Shubert

EDITORS **ARABIC** Mohamed Al Hammadi   **KOREA** Sun-ok Nam
BRAZIL Matthew Shirts   **LATIN AMERICA** Omar López
BULGARIA Krassimir Drumev   **LITHUANIA** Frederikas Jansonas
CHINA Ye Nan   **NETHERLANDS/BELGIUM** Aart Aarsbergen
CROATIA Hrvoje Prćić   **NORDIC COUNTRIES** Karen Gunn
CZECHIA Tomáš Tureček   **POLAND** Martyna Wojciechowska
ESTONIA Erkki Peetsalu   **PORTUGAL** Gonçalo Pereira
FRANCE François Marot   **ROMANIA** Cristian Lascu
GERMANY Erwin Brunner   **RUSSIA** Alexander Grek
GREECE Maria Atmatzidou   **SERBIA** Igor Rill
HUNGARY Tamás Schlosser   **SLOVENIA** Marija Javornik
INDONESIA Hendra Noor Saleh   **SPAIN** Josep Cabello
ISRAEL Daphne Raz   **TAIWAN** Roger Pan
ITALY Marco Cattaneo   **THAILAND** Kowit Phadungruangkij
JAPAN Shigeo Otsuka   **TURKEY** Nesibe Bat

ADVERTISING 161 Sixth Avenue, New York, NY, 10013; Phone: 212-610-5500; Fax: 212-610-5505
EXECUTIVE VICE PRESIDENT AND WORLDWIDE PUBLISHER: Claudia Malley. NATIONAL ADVERTISING DIRECTOR: Robert Amberg. VICE PRESIDENT MARKETING: Jenifer Berman. VICE PRESIDENT BUSINESS AND OPERATIONS: Margaret Schmidt. NATIONAL MANAGER: Tammy Abraham
INTERNATIONAL MANAGING DIRECTOR: Charlie Attenborough. DIRECTORS: Nadine Heggie *(International)*, Rebecca Hill *(Marketing)*, David Middis *(British Isles)*
CONSUMER MARKETING VICE PRESIDENT WORLDWIDE: Terrence Day. DIRECTORS: Christina C. Alberghini *(Member Services)*, Anne Barker *(Renewals)*, Richard Brown *(New Business)*, John MacKethan *(Financial Planning and Retail Sales)*, John A. Seeley *(International)*

Relax with *panache* in our award-winning
Heathrow Clubhouse. Enjoy a gourmet
meal in The Brasserie or a bespoke cocktail
at the bar, then spruce yourself up in our
Bumble and bumble hair salon. There's
even a library and free Wi-Fi for those last
minute emails. And when it's time to fly,
put your feet up and your head down in
one of the longest fully flat beds in the sky.
Oh, the *joie de* flying Upper Class. Discover
more at virginatlantic.com/experience
Your airline's either got it or it hasn't.

Before bon voyage
comes bon vivant.

upperclass

virgin atlantic

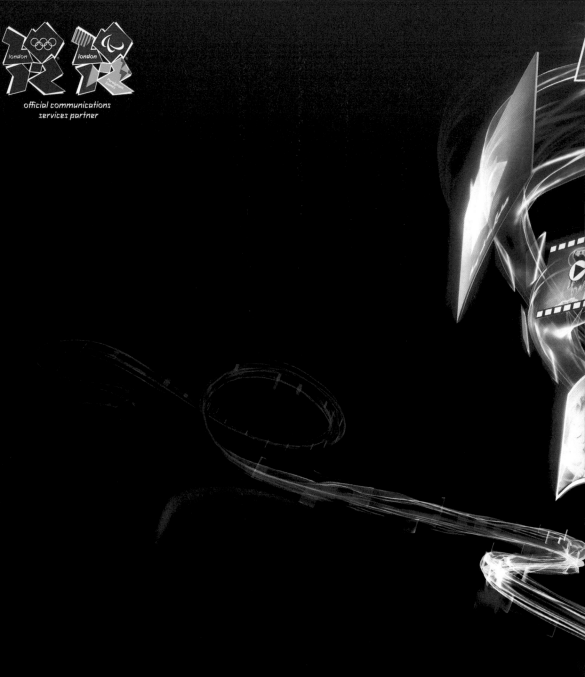

BT

Bringing it all together

VISIONS

Mexico
Surfacing in warm winter waters off the Baja California coast, a gray whale flashes its baleen plates by a boat. The area's lagoons and bays provide breeding and calving grounds for the giants, which migrate from as far north as the Bering Sea.

PHOTO: CHRISTOPHER SWANN, BIOSPHOTO

Cuba
Enjoying the storm, a boy dances in a downspout's downpour along a narrow street in Old Havana—a centuries-old part of the city that has been named a UNESCO World Heritage site. Restoration of the area's buildings is proceeding slowly.

PHOTO: DESMOND BOYLAN, REUTERS

Look for *Visions of Earth*—the book—now available in stores.

United Kingdom
A lone mute swan
stretches its wings upon
a brook as the mists
of dawn filter through
London's Richmond Park.
By tradition, the British
monarch has the right
to claim ownership of
unmarked birds of this
species in open water.

PHOTO: ALEX SABERI

↖ **Order prints** of *National Geographic* photos online at **PrintsNGS.com.**

Where does fine taste come from? The evidence points to a latitude of 55.45°N and a longitude of 06.16°W. There lies Islay, the most southern of the Inner Hebridean islands. And home to Bowmore, Islay's first Single Malt, dating back two centuries.

Is there such a thing as geography of taste?

On the question of taste, Bowmore gets off to a fine start. Islay basks in the warm Gulf Stream, so its climate is perfect, and the earth rich and fertile. Then, once nature's conferred its benefits, our craftsmen get to work. They fire the kilns fuelled by the peat Islay is famed for. And tend the mellow, oak casks with a know-how that could only come from experience.

The result? A highly awarded Single Malt, described as 'a clinic on how to finish a malt in sherry casks'. One with classic Bowmore smokiness, complemented by dark chocolate and raisin aromas.

So, is there such a thing as 'geography of taste'? We couldn't possibly comment. But might we suggest you test it for yourself?

To enjoy a dram, find your nearest bar at bowmore.com/find-your-dram

BOWMORE
ISLAY
SINGLE MALT
SCOTCH WHISKY

ISLAY TO THE CORE

VISIONS | **YOUR SHOT**

This page features two photographs: one chosen by our editors and one chosen by our readers via online voting. For more information, go to *ngm.com/yourshot.*

EDITORS' CHOICE **Jayne Harris-Waller** Oxford, England

On a spring trip to the seaside, Harris-Waller, 27, saw this couple relaxing outside their Exmouth beach hut—"a fleeting image of archetypal British culture. The blazing blue sky emphasized the intense man-made colors of the huts. It was the moment I felt the long winter was finally over."

READERS' CHOICE

Kathy Parker
Robe, Australia

"Living on a farm in South Australia," says Parker, 31, "we find a lot of blue-tongue lizards in our yard. This one came to our back door courtesy of Tiger, our son's cat, who bravely brings us all sorts of amazing creatures—alive and unharmed—for inspection and approval."

AVIVA

"It felt
amazing

to have
my

15
seconds
of fame"

As part of our You are the
Big Picture campaign, we're
not only giving people
like Laura the chance to see
their picture projected live
on to London's National Theatre,
we're also giving them the opportunity
to tell the world what matters to them.

In return, we'll donate £2 to
Save the Children projects helping street
children in India.

Upload your photo at
facebook.com/Aviva

Laura Seddon, Coventry

For Elijah, our home's vacuum cleaner hose became a system to repeat his favorite public-address announcements.

Echolilia All parents love their children. But what do you do when you can't connect with them? In my case, I started making photographs of, and with, my son Elijah, who has autism spectrum disorder. This series—the title is from "echolalia," a clinical term for the mimicking aspect of his condition—shows the bridges we've built on our shared journey of wonder, discovery, and understanding.

We began this project when Eli was five. He was doing well at school but fixating on odd things, lashing out, speaking repetitively. My wife and I couldn't figure him out. Then I started taking pictures of him around the house. It was an instinctive act for a photographer: Point your camera at something in order to make sense of it. But a curious thing happened. As I documented what Eli was doing and creating, he became interested in the images I was making. I was learning how he thinks; he was learning what I like and value.

We soon had a system. Eli would do something unusual, one of us would notice, and we'd make a photo of it together. The pictures we took over three years were more raw and feral than anything I'd done as an editorial or advertising photographer. And more personal. This is, after all, the story of a father and his son.

THE PHOTOGRAPHER

Timothy Archibald's book, Echolilia: Sometimes I Wonder, *was published last year by Echo Press. See more of his work at* timothyarchibald.com.

SAVE ON PETROL NOT ON PERFORMANCE

i-stop*, our award winning engine-idling-stop system, improves fuel economy and CO_2 emissions. What's more, it gets you started in just 0.35 seconds, faster than any other comparable system.

It's particularly quick because the engine is always primed to restart. In fact, our engineers took inspiration from cyclists who position their pedals in a way that allows them to get going immediately. This unconventional approach has resulted in smart, fuel-saving technology that's so responsive you'll barely notice it's there.

The Mazda3 with i-stop; it won't leave you sitting at the lights.

DEFY CONVENTION

www.mazda.co.uk/stories

The official fuel consumption figures in mpg (l/100km) for the Mazda3 range (excl. MPS): Urban 26.7 (10.6) – 53.3 (5.3), Extra Urban 46.3 (6.1) – 72.4 (3.9), Combined 37.2 (7.6) – 64.2 (4.4). CO_2 emissions (g/km) 176 – 117.

*i-stop is available on Mazda3 2.0 5dr Sport only. Model shown is Mazda3 2.0 5dr Sport. OTR £19,005. Model shown features optional Mica paint (£420)

One Christmas we collected logs at a park and brought them home to use in our fireplace. Eli became obsessed with the shape of one and asked us not to burn it. I wanted to make some pictures with the log outside, but he took it into his room instead. As a photographer—and as a parent—I often like to let him lead.

Why Eli put these needle-nose pliers in his mouth I can't tell you. Maybe they reminded him of a bird's beak. To me, their sharp edges and his bare skin imply danger. Working with him, I find myself questioning boundaries. Am I his parent now or his collaborator? Am I empowering my kid, or am I overpowering him?

At a point in this series I started to focus on the settings we were using. Our living room is great because it gets so much light. We cleared the floor and took all the toys out of this plastic bin. Eli was delighted to learn he could get his whole body into it—so he curled up and pretended he was sleeping inside an egg.

I sometimes think of Eli as having a huge book of odd knowledge in his head. In real time the contents can be hard for people to understand. But when he sat with a big dictionary in his lap, hands spread as though reading braille, I saw the metaphor come to life. The blur is courtesy of a one-second exposure.

My mission is
s to kayak in the Indian ocean and
bask in the warm South African sun

South Africa
It's Possible

Follow Jamie on his mission to South Africa

We are sending a team of celebrities on a mission to discover the
variety of experiences available in South Africa. Jamie Theakston is
embarking on an adventure and sport trip, to follow his progress, share
his experiences and plan your own South African mission, visit
www.southafrica.net

let us guide you
Africa Collection

Jamie Theakston's trip is available from Africa Collection

www.africacollection.co.uk

An adult tarantula reaches the top of a glass pane.

Seen through an electron microscope, a tarantula's foot has sticky hairs and what some believe are thin, silk-secreting spigots.

Spider Spigots

Tarantulas are among the largest, most primitive, best known spiders. Yet how these hairy crawlers negotiate steep, slippery surfaces has been a tangled web for arachnologists. Some say climbing tarantulas—too heavy and fragile to rely on sticky foot hairs as other spiders do—release silk from their feet when they lose their grip. Others insist silk comes only from abdominal spinnerets; the feet merely distribute it when a tarantula goes vertical.

Enter Newcastle University biologist Claire Rind. This year she and her colleagues studied several species, including a Chilean rose (above) that they put in a glass tank lined with microscope slides. When the bin was tilted and jostled, the spider slipped but hung on. A video verified that only its feet had touched the slides, which bore silken footprints. The final test was a hard look at molted exoskeletons, whose feet had silk traces and what looked like nozzles among the setae, or hairs.

Though some experts remain skeptical about silk-shooting foot spigots, Rind says she's pushing on. The next strands she hopes to unstick: whether nozzles exist on smaller or juvenile tarantulas—or even on other spider species. *—Jeremy Berlin*

Why can't an estate be stylish as well as spacious?

The All New Hyundai *i40* Tourer

The Hyundai i40 Tourer's fluidic design means it's unlike any other estate. But its stunning appearance isn't at the expense of space or comfort. It has class-leading leg and headroom in the front, with a memory function for the electric multi-adjustable driver's seat'. Two-stage reclining rear seats make long journeys exceptionally comfortable in the back too. And with an impressively large boot, the i40 has more than enough space for whatever you need to carry. As you can see, an estate can have a style all of its own.

Prices start at £18,395*
Benefit in kind tax from 13%, £83.81 per month** (40% income tax bracket)
Find out more at hyundai.co.uk

Bring this ad to life with the i40 app for iPhone® 4 and Android™ 2.2 & above

Shuttles' Last Trip

After roughly 30 years of service, the remaining space shuttles are headed for the final frontier: retirement. Museums around the country have been clamoring for a chance to take one home.

When the Apollo program ended, the Smithsonian had right of first refusal for surplus NASA artifacts, from astronaut diapers to lunar landers. But for the shuttles, NASA issued a special proposal. Museums that wanted an orbiter could apply for one, but they had to say how the ship would be displayed, how their exhibit would "inspire the American public," and—most important—how they would raise the $28.8 million needed for cleaning and transport.

As a result, the California Science Center will soon be one of only four museums to house a space shuttle (map below): *Endeavour* is due to land in Los Angeles in 2012. "We have the honor of being stewards of something that we all hold as part of our national heritage," says the museum's aerospace science curator, Kenneth E. Phillips. "It's an overwhelming feeling." —*Victoria Jaggard*

ENTERPRISE
New York, NY

ENDEAVOUR
Los Angeles, CA   UNITED
STATES

DISCOVERY
Chantilly, VA

ATLANTIS
Kennedy Space Center, FL

Discovery is taken
apart for a thorough
cleaning at Florida's
Kennedy Space Center
before its eventual
display in Virginia.

PHOTO: CHRISTOPHER MORRIS. NGM MAPS

Skydivers reach
a top speed
of more than
100 miles an hour.

Cranberry Nation

Whether plopped from a can (above) or plated as a freshly made compote, cranberries will grace many an American table on November 24. The scarlet fruit wasn't tied to Thanksgiving until the 19th century, says food historian Andrew F. Smith, who cites an 1817 newspaper reference. Yet it's been part of our diet since the 1600s, when Native Americans introduced it to English settlers. Today the tart berries are marketed year-round in both juice and dried form. They're also touted as a health food, because they can keep bacteria from clinging to the urinary tract and may even play a role in cancer prevention.

One of just a smattering of fruits indigenous to the U.S. (blueberries and pawpaws are among the others), cranberries are harvested "dry," by lawn-mower-like machines that comb the vines, or "wet," which involves flooding a bog with water and corralling the floating fruit. Native to the Northeast, cranberries also flourish in developed bogs farther west. In fact, with 18,000 acres, Wisconsin now reaps more of the crimson crop than any other state. —Catherine Zuckerman

THE LIST

The Relative Price of Gas

The price of crude oil doesn't differ much worldwide, so why such a range in gas prices? Subsidies can make fuel more affordable, as in Venezuela; heavy taxes put Turkey on top and are the norm in many European nations with extensive public transit. —Alexandra Tilsley

Average price per gallon in U.S. dollars, June 2011

10.02
Istanbul, Turkey

8.39
London, U.K.

5.41
Toronto, Canada

4.00
New York City, U.S.

1.11
Cairo, Egypt

0.06
Caracas, Venezuela

Every story needs a book.
Make yours.

Turning your pictures into a beautiful book is easy with Blurb.
Our free tools give you as much creative freedom as you like.
Our process produces a book as well made as any in your bookstore —
whether it's one copy or one for everyone you know. And we'll get it
in your hands in as little as a week. Our platform even makes it simple
to share or sell your creations online.

Get started at blurb.com

A harbor seal named Henry is outfitted for sensory studies at a lab in Rostock, Germany.

Whiskers at Work

Not much gets by a harbor seal. That's because its whiskers, or vibrissae, pick up highly detailed data about the animal's environment. A seal's snout hairs protrude from follicles containing about ten times as many nerve endings as a rat's sensitive whiskers. Sensory biologist Wolf Hanke of the University of Rostock says seal vibrissae have adapted over 25 million-plus years to read minute changes in water movement.

Hanke and colleagues study this phenomenon with Henry, a trained harbor seal (above). Wearing a blindfold and headphones, Henry has shown that he can detect the traces of an object in calm water even 30 seconds after the object has passed. And the latest trials reveal that he can also distinguish among shapes and sizes—using just his whiskers. Other species likely share this ability, which, Hanke posits, helps seals nab darting fish. It even lets them "see" the meatiest prey in the murkiest waters, for a more fruitful chase. *—Jennifer S. Holland*

KOI STORY Legend has it that a fish named Hanako was the world's longest lived. After swimming for 226 years in Japan, the story goes, the scarlet koi died in 1977. Her scales were said to determine her elderly age—a notion that holds water with science today. Much as trees have rings, fish have microscopic "zones" within their scales that reflect seasonal growth patterns. In summer, when food is abundant, fish grow quickly and produce wide zones. Winter lines are narrow. A pair of zones represents one year. In Hanako's case, adding them up must have taken an eternity. *—Catherine Zuckerman*

PHOTO: WOLF HANKE, MARINE SCIENCE CENTER, UNIVERSITY OF ROSTOCK. ART: MARC JOHNS

WITH GORE-TEX® PRODUCTS INSIDE

YOU CAN STEP OUT IN COMFORT OUTSIDE.

London, 12°C. A cloudy and drizzly afternoon. Lots of puddles all over the pavements. Just perfect conditions to spend some time strolling the city. Provided, that is, you have the right footwear Shoes engineered with GORE-TEX® product technology provide the best combination of high breathability and durable waterproof protection to stay comfortable and to discover every corner of the city with dry feet. Visit **www.gore-tex.com** and experience more.

Highly Breathable

Durably Waterproof

Fall Far

Clarks

www.clarks.com

GUARANTEED
TO KEEP YOU DRY

GORE·TEX® PRODUCTS

Experience more...

Water in a cumulus cloud of this size weighs about as much as 400 elephants.

1 mile

1 mile 1 mile

N. IRELAND (U.K.)

★Dublin

IRELAND

County with protected bog site

0 mi   80

0 km   80

Turf Tug-of-War
It's long been a staple of Irish rural life: the earthy warmth of burning peat. For centuries families relied on turf bricks cut from raised bogs (above) and dried for fuel. Now a move by the European Union to enforce a 1997 directive to protect these disappearing ancient habitats—rich in decomposing plants and rare species—has turf cutters bristling.

The EU designation of dozens of large bogs for conservation, part of a push to protect environmental diversity, went largely unenforced due to rural Irish sensitivities. But evidence of extensive cutting led the EU to threaten heavy fines last year. Industrial interests continued to cut, citing jobs. A tentative peace was reached this past summer, with contractors agreeing to halt activity for the rest of the year. But the ground remains unsteady; Irish legislator and turf cutter Luke Flanagan promises a fresh fight next year. —Erin Friar McDermott

PHOTO: CHRIS HILL. NGM MAPS. GRAPHIC: NGM ART

Golf All Year Round

PORTUGAL

The beauty of simplicity

isitportugal.com

Portugal

urope's West Coast

NEXT

Umbrellas 2.0
We trash countless umbrellas each year, grumbling about how easily they flip or fail us in strong storms. Now several novel designs attempt to confront the classic canopy's downfalls. To avoid inversion, Dutch designer Gerwin Hoogendoorn made his Senz umbrella (above) aerodynamic enough to withstand wind tunnel gusts of 70 miles an hour. Greig Brebner, a tall New Zealander alarmed by the onslaught of eye-level spokes he faced while living in London, came up with the Blunt umbrella, with enclosed points that make it both safer and stronger. And for that romantic stroll in the rain, there's even a tandem umbrella.

The boldest revision comes from U.S. entrepreneur Alan Kaufman: Nubrella, a transparent bubble that rests on one's shoulders or, soon, in a backpack. Sure, it looks a bit odd. But "in real bad weather," says Kaufman, "not many people are looking at you." —*Amanda Fiegl*

Bubble concept
Avoid the elements—
or turn heads at least
—the hands-free way.

Going tandem
The double-broad
canopy offers full
coverage for two.

PHOTO: REBECCA HALE, NGM STAFF. ART: JASON LEE

Campo Viejo™

live uncorked

This Baby May Well Live to 100

SEVEN BILLION

Somewhere, an October newborn just pushed global population past seven billion, according to the United Nations Population Fund. If the birth occurred in Japan, France, the United States, or a handful of other wealthy nations, that landmark child will likely reach another milestone: a 100th birthday. Today, says Danish epidemiologist Kaare Christensen, more than half the babies in such well-off places are expected to become centenarians.

A typical life in an industrialized country is now about 80 years long—three decades longer than it was a century ago. In contrast, life expectancy in sub-Saharan Africa is a mere 53 years. Infant health worldwide has generally improved; the global gap persists largely due to gains in seniors' health in developed countries. Earlier diagnoses of illnesses, especially heart disease, and more accessible buildings have helped improve late-life comfort and mobility. As a result, says Christensen, most of those lucky enough to reach 100 "would like to have another birthday."

How best to join the hundred-plus club? There's no single answer. But most studies of centenarians show that if you're a woman, a nonsmoker, wealthy, or slim, you're off to a good start. —*Brad Scriber*

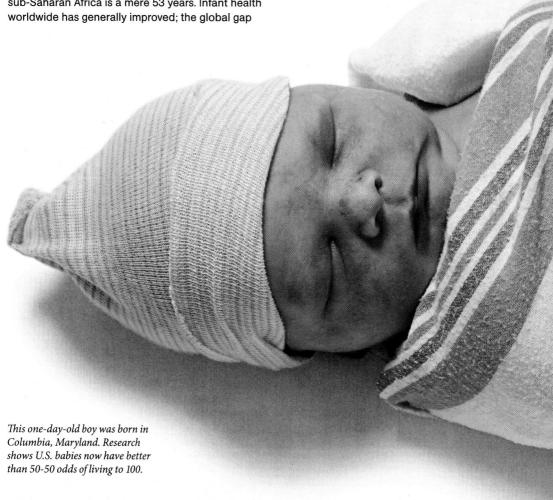

This one-day-old boy was born in Columbia, Maryland. Research shows U.S. babies now have better than 50-50 odds of living to 100.

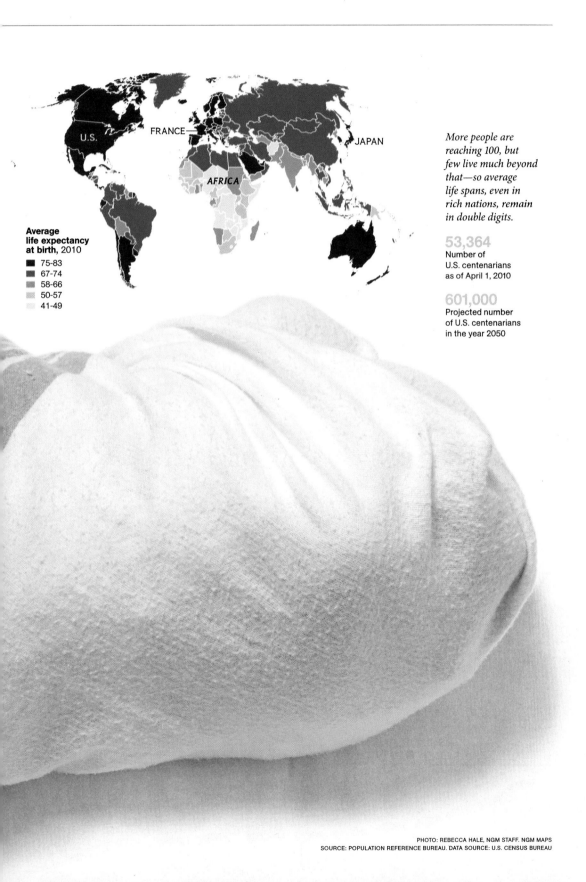

FRANCE
U.S.
JAPAN

AFRICA

**Average
life expectancy
at birth,** 2010

- 75-83
- 67-74
- 58-66
- 50-57
- 41-49

*More people are
reaching 100, but
few live much beyond
that—so average
life spans, even in
rich nations, remain
in double digits.*

53,364
Number of
U.S. centenarians
as of April 1, 2010

601,000
Projected number
of U.S. centenarians
in the year 2050

PHOTO: REBECCA HALE, NGM STAFF. NGM MAPS
SOURCE: POPULATION REFERENCE BUREAU. DATA SOURCE: U.S. CENSUS BUREAU

The moon's surface area is roughly 15 million square miles—only 3 million more than Africa's.

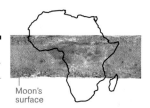

Moon's surface

Algae Solar Cells

The secret to greener, more efficient solar energy? It may lie in the shell of a single-celled, 100-million-year-old life form called a diatom. Best known as the ubiquitous algae at the base of aquatic food chains, diatoms have intricate shells—covered with a lattice of pores for optimal light capture—that are winning the attention of nanotechnologists. Chemical engineer Greg Rorrer is growing diatoms with semi-conducting materials infused into their skeletons. Pumped into solar cells, they create a powerhouse unit that's 50 percent more efficient. Not bad for an old phytoplankton. —*Gretchen Parker*

The single-celled diatoms below—the likes of which are found in oceans worldwide— were collected with a plank-ton net in San Francisco Bay.

PHOTO: DAVID LIITTSCHWAGER
GRAPHIC: ÁLVARO VALIÑO

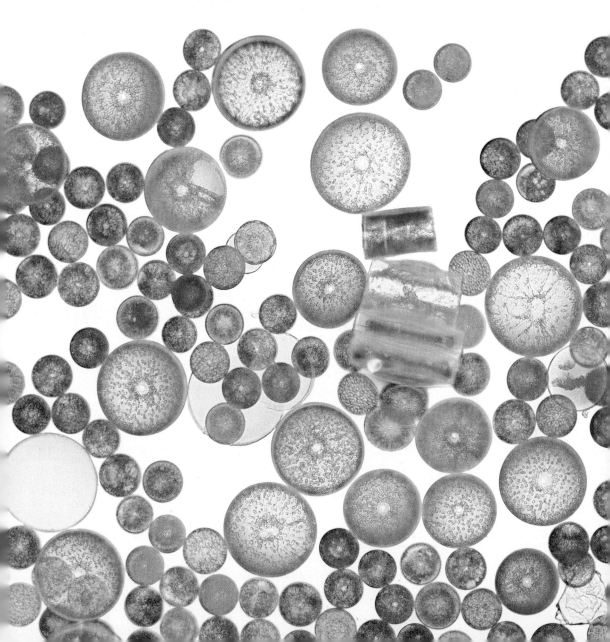

UGC 1810

Celestial Valentine

Hubble Space Telescope astronomers recently focused the instrument's powerful eye on a pair of galaxies known as Arp 273, which had spun themselves into something surreally terrestrial: a rose.

What you're seeing on this page is an interaction that occurred a few hundred million years ago, as the lower galaxy (UGC 1813) dived through the outside arms of the upper one (UGC 1810). Like a bloom unfolding, the arms of the larger galaxy were stretched apart by the gravitational pull of the smaller one. Hot blue stars formed from the compressed gas and dust.

This image may be unusual, but the action it captured is not. Astronomers say most galaxies collide with another at some point in their lifetimes. Two often merge after an average mutual orbit of 500 million years—romance in the heavens we now can see clearly for ourselves.

—Gretchen Parker

UGC 1813

The "rose galaxy," or Arp 273, is more than 300 million light-years away from Earth, in the Andromeda constellation.

IMAGE: NASA

Istanbul, Turkey

TAKE TIME TO

SEE THE WORLD

FROM HIS PERSPECTIVE.

HILTON HHONORS™ TRANSFORMS YOUR POINTS INTO MEMORIES YOU CAN'T HELP BUT SHARE.

Looking for an eye-opening experience? Whether you visit Turkey or New York City, your HHonors points can lead to new sights in 82 countries around the world. And from the Conrad Istanbul to the Hilton Garden Inn Times Square, there are more than 3,750 hotels worldwide from ten distinct brands. You'll always find the perfect hotel for every budget and any occasion. So, get ready to see the world from many new points of view.

• Enrol at HHonors.com •

africa's water loves treatment

In Africa, Guinea worm cases have been drastically reduced since 1986 by using our Abate® larvicide: an efficient water treatment product that kills insect larvae and makes contaminated sources safe again. When eradicating life-threatening diseases means helping communities to grow stronger, it's because at BASF, we create chemistry. **www.basf.com/chemistry**

International Year of
CHEMISTRY

BASF is a Global Sponsor

■□·**BASF**

The Chemical Company

Scanning Zebras

For scientists tracking zebras, point and shoot now involves a camera instead of a tranquilizer gun. That's because they can now use those distinctive black and white stripes to count a population, bar code style.

In the field, researchers snap a photo of a zebra and upload it to a computer with StripeSpotter, a software application developed by the University of Illinois at Chicago and Princeton University. On a screen they focus on the flank, where each stripe gets broken down into vertical strands of pixels. Those combinations are as unique to each zebra as fingerprints are to humans. A database scan quickly shows if the zebra is a new find.

StripeSpotter has been used on Grevy's and plains zebras and is being tested on tigers and giraffes. It's also open to citizen scientists: Check a zebra's ID at *code.google.com/p/ stripespotter.*

—Erin Friar McDermott

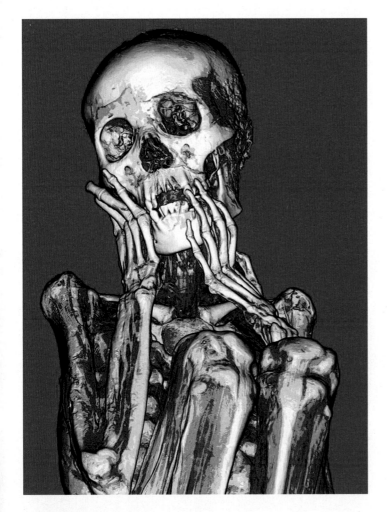

3-D Mummy

A young woman was scanned this past spring with the newest high-resolution CT technology. She came to the U.S. from the highlands of central Peru—where she had died some 550 years ago. Now she's the first complete mummy whose health has been probed by radiologists using such detailed CT images.

The subject appears to be in mid-scream, but she was actually bound in this position before burial. Smithsonian anthropologist Aleš Hrdlička found her in 1913 in a looted cave tomb. Today her naturally mummified body resides in San Diego's Museum of Man.

U.S. Navy medical personnel performed the scan and produced this image (bones are white, soft tissue is red). Radiologists have already identified signs of tuberculosis or a fungal lung infection. As they look deeper, they hope to better understand nutrition and diseases around the time of the Spanish conquest of South America. When they're not caring for live patients, that is. *—A. R. Williams*

The treasure's flashy ornaments announced the status of men like this aristocrat riding to war. At the battlefield he would have dismounted and joined the rest of the warriors as they formed a defensive wall with their shields. Combat was gory, conducted at close range with swords, spears, and axes.

Magical Mystery Treasure

Buried in the English countryside.
Anglo-Saxon in origin.
Who hid it and why?

BY CAROLINE ALEXANDER • PHOTOGRAPHS BY ROBERT CLARK

ART BY DANIEL DOCIU

The 3,500 pieces of treasure unearthed on a Staffordshire farm in 2009 were mostly golden adornments for war gear, like the scabbard pendant inlaid with garnets and blue glass at left. Some were twisted or broken as if they had been forced into a small space.

One day, or perhaps one night, in the late seventh century an unknown party traveled along an old Roman road that cut across an uninhabited heath fringed by forest in the Anglo-Saxon kingdom of Mercia. Possibly they were soldiers, or then again maybe thieves—the remote area would remain notorious for highwaymen for centuries—but at any rate they were not casual travelers. Stepping off the road near the rise of a small ridge, they dug a pit and buried a stash of treasure in the ground.

For 1,300 years the treasure lay undisturbed, and eventually the landscape evolved from forest clearing to grazing pasture to working field. Then treasure hunters equipped with metal detectors—ubiquitous in Britain—began to call on farmer Fred Johnson, asking permission to walk the field. "I told one I'd lost a wrench and asked him to find that," Johnson says. Instead, on July 5, 2009, Terry Herbert came to the farmhouse door and announced to Johnson that he had found Anglo-Saxon treasure.

The Staffordshire Hoard, as it was quickly dubbed, electrified the general public and Anglo-Saxon scholars alike. Spectacular discoveries, such as the royal finds at Sutton Hoo in Suffolk, had been made in Anglo-Saxon burial sites. But the treasure pulled from Fred Johnson's field was novel—a cache of gold, silver, and garnet objects from early Anglo-Saxon times and from one of the most important kingdoms of the era. Moreover, the quality and style of the intricate filigree and cloisonné decorating the objects were extraordinary, inviting heady comparisons to such legendary treasures as the Lindisfarne Gospels or the Book of Kells.

Once cataloged, the hoard was found to contain some 3,500 pieces representing hundreds of complete objects. And the items that could be securely identified presented a striking

Contributing writer Caroline Alexander wrote the June 2008 cover story about Stonehenge. Robert Clark drove more than 3,000 miles to complete his 30th National Geographic *story. This is Daniel Dociu's first assignment for the magazine.*

On a farm near his home Terry Herbert shows off the metal detector that led him to the gold. "I just couldn't stop the items from coming out of the ground," he says. He received half the treasure's assessed value of almost $5.3 million.

pattern. There were more than 300 sword-hilt fittings, 92 sword-pommel caps, and 10 scabbard pendants. Also noteworthy: There were no coins or women's jewelry, and out of the entire collection, the three religious objects appeared to be the only nonmartial pieces. Intriguingly, many of the items seemed to have been bent or broken. This treasure, then, was a pile of broken, elite, military hardware hidden 13 centuries ago in a politically and militarily turbulent region. The Staffordshire Hoard was thrilling and historic—but above all it was enigmatic.

CELTS, ROMAN COLONIZERS, Viking marauders, Norman conquerors—all came and went, leaving their mark on Britain's landscape, language, and character. But it is the six centuries of Anglo-Saxon rule, from shortly after the departure of the Roman colonizers, around A.D. 410, to the Norman Conquest in 1066, that most define what we now call England.

Barbarian tribes had been moving westward across Europe since the mid-third century and may have made raids on Britain around this time. In the early fifth century the restless tribes

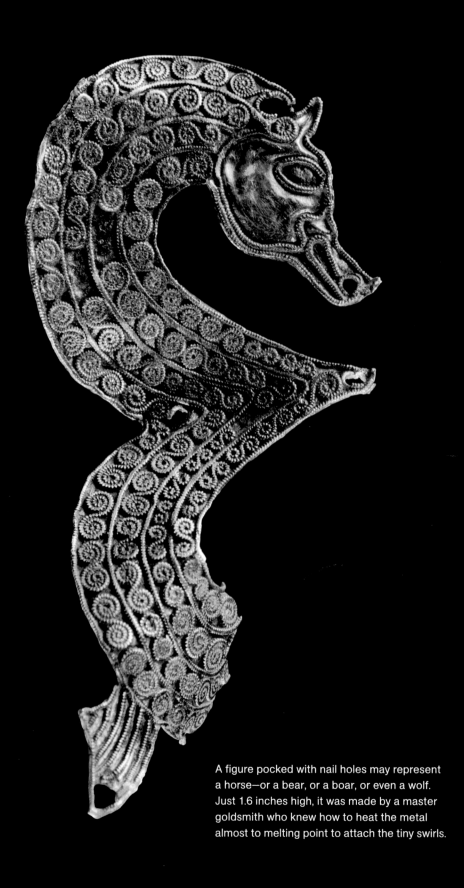

A figure pocked with nail holes may represent a horse—or a bear, or a boar, or even a wolf. Just 1.6 inches high, it was made by a master goldsmith who knew how to heat the metal almost to melting point to attach the tiny swirls.

menaced Rome, prompting it to withdraw garrisons from Britannia, the province it had governed for 350 years, to fight threats closer to home. As the Romans left, the Scotti and Picts, tribes to the west and north, began to raid across the borders. Lacking Roman defenders, Britons solicited Germanic troops from the continent as mercenaries. The Venerable Bede—whose *Ecclesiastical History of the English People,* written in the eighth century, is the most valuable source for this era— gives the year of the fateful invitation as around 450 and characterizes the soldiers as coming from "three very powerful Germanic tribes, the Saxons, Angles, and Jutes." Modern scholars locate the homelands of these tribes in Germany, the northern Netherlands, and Denmark.

Enticed by reports of the richness of the land and the "slackness of the Britons," the soldiers in the first three ships were followed by more, and soon, Bede noted, "hordes of these peoples eagerly crowded into the island and the number of foreigners began to increase to such an extent that they became a source of terror to the natives." The British monk Gildas, whose sixth-century treatise *On the Ruin of Britain* is the earliest surviving account of this murky period, describes the ensuing islandwide bloodshed and scorched-earth tactics at the hands of the invaders: "For the fire of vengeance…spread from sea to sea…and did not cease, until, destroying the neighbouring towns and lands, it reached the other side of the island."

According to Gildas, many in the "miserable remnant" of surviving native Britons fled or were enslaved. But archaeological evidence suggests that at least some post-Roman settlements adopted Germanic fashions in pottery and clothing and burial practices; in other words, British culture vanished at least in part through cultural assimilation. The extent of the Anglo-Saxons' appropriation of Britain is starkly revealed in their most enduring legacy, the English language. While much of Europe emerged from the post-Roman world speaking Romance languages— Spanish, Italian, and French derived from the Latin of the bygone Romans—the language that would define England was Germanic.

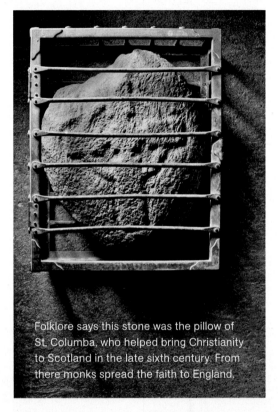

Folklore says this stone was the pillow of St. Columba, who helped bring Christianity to Scotland in the late sixth century. From there monks spread the faith to England.

THE DISCOVERY OF A TREASURE HOARD in an English field was not in itself remarkable. Such finds surface everywhere in Britain. Coins, silver objects cut up for scrap metal, dumps of weapons, even a magnificent silver dinner service—all from British, Roman, or Viking times—have been found in the soil. In the Anglo-Saxon epic *Beowulf* the warrior Sigemund has killed a dragon guarding "dazzling spoils," and the aged hero Beowulf battles a dragon guarding gold and "garnered jewels" laid in the ground.

Treasure was buried for many reasons: to keep it out of enemy hands, to "bank" a fortune, to serve as a votive offering. Given the era's scant documentation, the motive behind the burial of the Staffordshire Hoard is best surmised from the hoard itself. The first clue is its military character, which suggests that the assemblage was not a grab bag of loot. The nature of the hoard accords with the *(Continued on page 56)*

How England Began

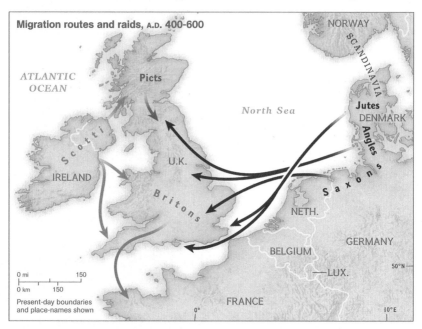

Migration routes and raids, A.D. 400–600

The Staffordshire treasure was created at a time of upheaval. After Roman rule ended, Germanic warriors helped the Britons beat back the Picts and Scotti (above). The Angles, Saxons, and Jutes then turned on their local allies and carved out kingdoms (right). As this fragmented land became a state under one king, literature flourished, coins were minted, and people adopted Christianity. In 1066 Norman invaders defeated Harold II, England's last Anglo-Saxon ruler.

BRONZE HEAD OF THE ROMAN EMPEROR HADRIAN, SECOND CENTURY A.D.

KING ARTHUR DEPICTED IN AN EARLY 15TH-CENTURY TAPESTRY FRAGMENT

GOLD AND GARNET BUTTONS FROM THE STAFFORDSHIRE HOARD

A.D. 400   500   600   700

ca 450
Angles, Saxons, and Jutes arrive in England following the end of Roman rule, ca 410.

Early sixth century
The legendary Roman-British leader King Arthur is said to have lived in this era.

Seventh century
Mercia develops into one of the three biggest kingdoms in England.

Mid-seventh century
Anglo-Saxon royal treasure is buried in the hull of a ship at Sutton Hoo.

ca 650-700
The Staffordshire Hoard, a cache of military hardware, is buried.

Greatest extent of
Anglo-Saxon authority,
ca 600-850

= = = = Road

0 mi   80
0 km   80

Modern spellings used

Edinburgh

Holy Island
(Lindisfarne)

Melrose

GREAT

HADRIAN'S WALL

Battle of
Heavenfield
634

North Sea

NORTHUMBRIA

York

Kells
Monastery

Isle of Man

Irish Sea

B R I T A I N

Chester

Lincoln

I R E L A N D

Lichfield

**Staffordshire
Hoard**

Trent

Repton

Tamworth

Thetford

EAST
ANGLIA

WELSH
LANDS

M E R C I A

WATLING STREET

Sutton
Hoo

Cirencester

Thames

ESSEX

London

W E S S E X

KENT

Dover

Ilchester

SUSSEX

Battle of
Hastings
1066

Exeter

English Channel

GRAVESTONE THAT MAY SHOW AN EARLY
VIKING RAID AT LINDISFARNE, ENGLAND

A SCENE IN THE LATE 11TH-CENTURY BAYEUX
TAPESTRY SHOWING THE BATTLE OF HASTINGS

800   900   1000   1100

ca Eighth century
Beowulf, an Anglo-Saxon epic, is
written in Old
English.

ca 793
Viking attacks
begin; they
continue into the
11th century.

Tenth century
England unifies
following the reign
of Alfred the Great,
who died in 899.

1066
The Battle of Hastings and the Norman Conquest end
Anglo-Saxon rule.

JEROME N. COOKSON, AMANDA
HOBBS, AND MARGUERITE B.
HUNSIKER, NGM STAFF. SOURCES:
KEVIN LEAHY, PORTABLE ANTIQUITIES
SCHEME; JAMES CAMPBELL

Hadrian's Wall, named for the second-century Roman emperor who built it, stretches 73 miles across Britain. It separated the civilized realm of Rome from the "barbarians"—restless Picts in the north. As the Romans withdrew, the northern tribes stormed across the border.

and those who hate you flee from your face."

A strip of gold once studded with a gem bears the same biblical quotation in Latin on each side: Moses' declaration, translated above, as the Israelites journeyed out of Sinai. The object may have decorated the arm of a cross prized by recent converts to Christianity.

Crowning Glory

At left, an artist's vision of a helmet from the time of the treasure. Probably padded with horsehair or wool, the helmet cap was made of hammered iron for protection from slashing or thrusting blades. It could have included two pieces found in the hoard: an intricately worked cheek panel (below) and a horse's head (above), the decorative end of a crest, perhaps of horsehair.

(*Continued from page 47*) militarism of the Germanic tribes, which was impressive even to the military-minded Romans. The historian Tacitus, writing in the late first century, noted that "they conduct no business, public or private, except under arms," and that when a boy came of age, he was presented with a shield and spear—"the equivalent of our toga."

Warfare formed England. The consolidation of land gained by warfare and alliances was the likely origin of the tribal kingships of early Anglo-Saxon England. The first Mercians are thought to have been Angles who moved inland along the River Trent, establishing themselves in the valley in the vicinity of the hoard. Mercia was not only one of the most important of the seven principal Anglo-Saxon kingships into which England was roughly divided but also one of the most belligerent. Between A.D. 600 and 850 Mercia waged 14 wars with its neighbor Wessex, 11 with the Welsh, and 18 campaigns with other foes—and these are only the named conflicts.

The apex of Teutonic military craft was the long cutting sword. Averaging about three feet, blades were pattern welded, a sophisticated technique by which twisted rods and strips of iron or steel were hammered together. Forged from this intricate folding, the polished blades rippled with chevron or herringbone patterns. As one appreciative recipient recorded in the early sixth century, they appear "to be grained with tiny snakes, and here such varied shadows play that you would believe the shining metal to be interwoven with many colours."

Modern studies of wounds on skeletons found in an Anglo-Saxon cemetery in Kent show that these beautiful swords also worked: "Male, aged 25-35 years…has a single linear cranial injury 16 cm long," states the clinical report. "The plane of the injury is almost vertically downwards."

The number of sword pommels in the Staffordshire Hoard, 92, roughly corresponds with the number of men noted as making up one nobleman's troop of retainers. The hoard, then, could represent the elite military gear that distinguished the retinue of a certain lord. Often a sword was issued by a lord to his retainers along with other equipment and even horses, together known as a heriot, repaid if the retainer died before his lord. In a will written in the tenth century a district official bequeaths "to my royal lord as a heriot four armlets of…gold, and four swords and eight horses, four with trappings and four without, and four helmets and four coats-of-mail and eight spears and eight shields." Swords were also buried with their warrior owners or passed down as family heirlooms.

But sometimes swords were buried without warriors. In a practice in northern Europe dating from the Bronze Age through Anglo-Saxon times, swords and other objects, many conspicuously valuable, were deposited in bogs, rivers, and streams as well as in the ground. "We can no longer see hoards only as piggy banks," says Kevin Leahy, an authority on Anglo-Saxon history who was entrusted with the task of cataloging the Staffordshire treasure. Ritual deposits, as opposed to caches buried for safekeeping, are found not only in Britain but also in Scandinavia, homeland of some of England's Germanic tribes. Significantly, many weapons—and sometimes other objects, such as a craftsman's tools —were, like the objects in the hoard, bent or broken before burial. Perhaps "killing" a weapon dispatched it to the land of spirits or rendered it a votive offering to the gods, its destruction representing the donor's irrevocable surrender of the valuable weapon's use.

"THIS IS A HOARD FOR MALE DISPLAY," says Nicholas Brooks, an emeritus historian at the University of Birmingham, who calls the glittering objects found in Staffordshire "bling for warrior companions of the king." Gold, weighing in at more than 11 pounds, accounts for nearly 75 percent of the metal in the hoard. According to Brooks, "the source is a mystery." The origin of most gold in England was ultimately Rome, whose later imperial currency had been based on the solidus, a solid gold coin. Imperial gold had fallen to the Germanic tribes as plunder following the sack of Rome, and caches found in England may have been recirculated and recycled. By the date of the Staffordshire Hoard, gold supplies were dwindling, and silver and silver alloy were being used instead. Similarly, the source of garnets—like gold, a striking feature of the hoard—had shifted, from India to Bohemia and Portugal.

Historian Guy Halsall has estimated the value of the hoard's gold in its day as equivalent to 800 solidi, about 80 horses' worth. Modern valuation of the find has been set at £3,285,000, or just under $5.3 million. In its own time, however, the hoard's worth was surely calibrated by other considerations. The gold dazzles, but from a practical point of view the most valuable part of the weaponry—"the long, sharp, pointy bit you killed people with," as Halsall notes dryly—is not present in the hoard, and it is possible that the sword blades were cannily retained for reuse.

Above all, the pieces in the hoard were forged and buried in a world in which mundane events and acts could be suffused with magic; misfortune, for instance, was commonly attributed to tiny darts fired by malicious elves, and many charms against attacks survive. The magic properties an object possessed trumped its material worth. Gold was valued not only for being precious but also because, alluring and indestructible, it was infused with magic, and therefore used in amulets. Germanic myths tell of the gods' great hall of gold, and as Christian churches and monasteries gained wealth, they acquired golden

occupation, faded as the Romans faded, and was vigorously reintroduced to Anglo-Saxon England by missionaries, most from Ireland and the Continent. There was a "perception of the conversion event as a spiritual battle," writes Karen Jolly, an authority on Anglo-Saxon popular religion. Conversion was a battle for the soul—effectively warfare, something the Germanic pagans

Handy Weapon

A jeweled pommel cap and rings brightened a hilt of bone or ivory (artist's rendition below) on a short, light sword known as a seax (SAY-aks). Generally wielded with one hand, the single-edged seax was more versatile than a full sword, serving as a hunting knife as well as a dagger. A blade of finely patterned iron and steel would have been a valued part of such a weapon, but none was included in the treasure.

This mysterious piece, almost four inches long, uses the same principle as the brake lights of modern cars: The wafflelike texture of the gold under each garnet increases the gem's reflectivity.

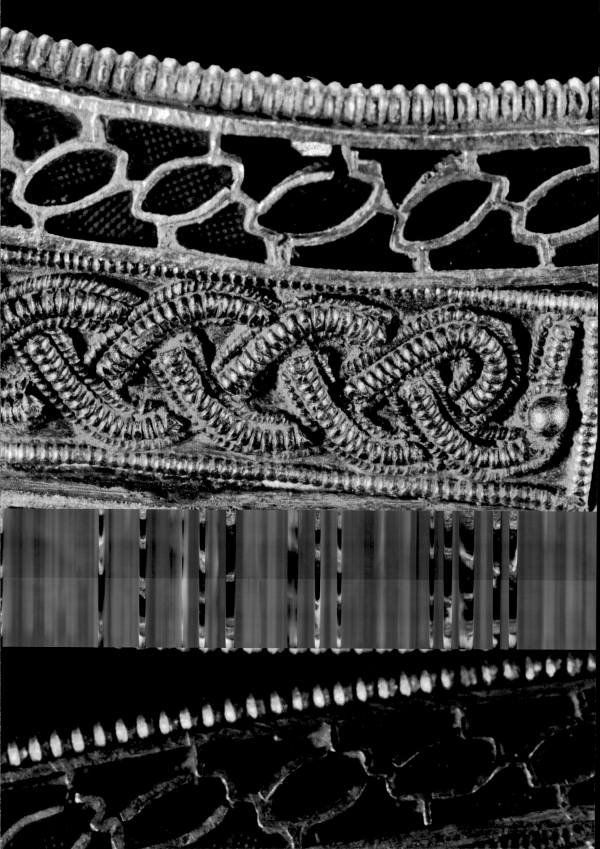

understood. And the cross was a militarily useful symbol that had figured dramatically in actual battles. Bede tells the story of the Northumbrian king Oswald, who before the Battle of Heavenfield against the Welsh in 634 "set up the sign of the holy cross and, on bended knees, prayed God to send heavenly aid to His worshippers in their dire need." He and his men then "gained the victory that their faith merited." Remarkably, one of the hoard's two crosses was determinedly bent and folded, like so many of the other pieces in the hoard. Was this to "kill" its military potency, as with the swords?

This possibility is made more compelling by the only other apparently nonmartial object: The slender strip of gold, inscribed on two sides with the same biblical quotation is, strikingly, also folded. *"[S]urge d[omi]ne disepentur inimici tui et [f]ugent qui oderunt te a facie tua*—Rise up, Lord, may your enemies be dispersed and those who hate you flee from your face." The quotation is from the Latin Vulgate text of Numbers 10:35 and the Psalm now numbered 68:1—verses that may have been put to unexpected use. In the *Life of Saint Guthlac,* written around 740, Guthlac is beset by demons, whereupon he "sang the first verse of the sixty-seventh psalm as if prophetically, 'Let God arise,' etc.: When they had heard this, at the same moment, quicker than words, all the hosts of demons vanished like smoke from his presence." Even the hoard's nonmartial objects, it seems, might have had militarily useful, magical functions.

THE MERCIANS WERE AGGRESSIVE border raiders—Mercia takes its name from the Old English *mierce,* meaning "frontier people"—which may account for the apparent range of regional styles in the hoard. "The hoard was found on a frontier zone, which is always interesting," Kevin Leahy says. "It was on the border between Mercia and Wales." In other words, in contested territory. Around 650, in Staffordshire's Trent Valley near Lichfield, an obscure battle was fought involving the Mercians and their Welsh neighbors. Much plunder was carried away—possibly down the old Roman road Watling Street, which leads

past the site where the Staffordshire Hoard was found. Event and place are commemorated in the Welsh poem "Marwnad Cynddylan—The Death Song of Cynddylan":

Grandeur in battle! Extensive spoils
Morial bore off from in front of Lichfield.
Fifteen hundred cattle from the front of battle;
four twenties of stallions and equal harness.
The chief bishop wretched in his four-cornered
house, the book-keeping monks did not protect.

A retinue of 80 horses and spoils from a "wretched" bishop (a detail that conjures the gold inscription and crosses): The poem offers a tempting explanation for the hoard, an explanation, alas, built from slender, circumstantial evidence that has happened to survive from an era from which most evidence was lost. We can conjure other teasing theories. Our unknown travelers may have chosen the burial spot because it was obscure—or because it was conspicuous. The burial might have had a marker for rediscovery, or it might have been intended as an offering hidden forever to all but their gods. The hoard may have been ransom, or booty, or a votive thanks. It may have been a collection of Anglo-Saxon heirlooms buried at a later time.

Today the vanished Mercian landscape is evoked by surviving Anglo-Saxon place-names, such as those ending with "leah" or "ley," meaning "open woodland," like Wyrley, or Lichfield itself, whose name roughly means the "common pasture in or beside the gray wood." The hoard burial site is now a grassy field where Fred Johnson grazes horses. Odds are we will never know the story behind the Staffordshire Hoard, but in a world without magic spells or dragons, would we understand it if we did? ☐

SECRETS OF THE LOST GOLD
Unravel more mysteries of lost gold of the Dark Ages during Expedition Week on **National Geographic Channel.** Check **natgeotv.com** for local listings.

Holy Relic

Inlaid with garnets, and perhaps glass, a gold cross (below) seems to have been crumpled before being buried with the rest of the treasure. The illustration at left depicts it as new, ready to adorn an altar or be carried into battle.

The
People
Who
Walk
With
Reindeer

SAMI

Ella-Li Spik of Jokkmokk, Sweden, is one of only a small percentage of Sami who grow up herding reindeer. She is part of a new generation with plans to attend college. "I want to explore the world," she says, "but I always want reindeer to be part of my life."

Sami herders follow the migrations of the reindeer as they move across northern Scandinavia
and Russia from their winter grazing grounds to cooler areas during the summer months.

By Jessica Benko   Photographs by Erika Larsen

Two hundred miles north of the Arctic Circle, near the jagged tips of Norway's crown, the sun does not set for weeks on end during the summer months, and the midnight sun bounces off fields of midsummer snow. The solstice comes and goes, but the Sami reindeer herders are too busy to pay much attention. "We're always in the middle of calf marking at this time," Ingrid Gaup says, referring to the yearly ritual in which the herding families carve their ancient marks into the ears of the new calves. In the Sami's homeland, spread across northern Norway, Sweden, Finland, and Russia, the notion of time is untethered from the cycles of the sun and is yoked instead to something far more important: the movement of the reindeer.

Sami herders call their work *boazovázzi,* which translates as "reindeer walker," and that's exactly what herders once did, following the fast-paced animals on foot or wooden skis as they sought out the best grazing grounds over hundreds of miles of terrain. Times have changed. Herders are now assigned to specific parcels of the reindeer's traditional grazing territories at designated times of the year. To make the lifestyle tenable, herders need expensive all-terrain vehicles (ATVs) and snowmobiles to maintain hundreds of miles of fences between territories and move large herds in accordance with land-use regulations—even when they clash with the instincts of the reindeer. As Ingrid's husband, Nils Peder Gaup, explains, "Reindeer think with the nose, not the eyes. They go with the wind."

Like many Sami of his generation, Nils Peder went to a compulsory boarding school where his native tongue was forbidden as part of the country's "Norwegianization" policies. Sami have been given more autonomy since then, but irretrievable damage was done to their language, now spoken by a minority. The Gaups are among the few Sami—a population estimated at around 70,000—who still herd reindeer.

Each June, after a long journey into the mountainous tundra of northern Norway, the Gaup family waits for the herd in tepee-like structures called *lávut.* They will spend sleepless nights marking the calves before moving the reindeer to their summer grazing grounds in the fjords.

At the first hint of the herd's arrival, the dogs in the encampment leap to their feet, ears erect. The herd spills over a far ridge, swelling like a stream down the mountainside. Other herders crest the rise on their ATVs, driving hundreds of thundering reindeer into a makeshift stockade. Small children, stiff as starfish in their snowsuits, toddle blithely inside the corral, unfazed by the reindeer stampede around them.

"I teach reindeer work to all of my children," says Nils Peder, as he guides his youngest son in marking a calf. His older children are so adept with sharp knives that they return calves to the mothers with only the faintest traces of blood on their ears. "Children must lift the culture," Nils Peder says, though he acknowledges the pressures of outside cultural influences. Herding families now live in modern homes equipped with Internet and television. Sara, the youngest of the Gaups' five children, spends much of the calf marking texting friends on her cell phone.

As herders face greater challenges, what path will girls like her choose? If reindeer herding disappears, Sami traditions may vanish too. The language itself reflects this powerful bond: The word for "herd" is *eallu;* the word for "life" is *eallin.* □

Sara Gaup, 14, is dressed for her confirmation. The garb that she and her father, Nils Peder Gaup, wear identifies their hometown as Kautokeino, Norway. The upturned tips of their reindeer-hide boots were designed to hook into skis.

Reindeer can spook suddenly, so Nils Peder kneels calmly in the midst of the beloved herd on which his livelihood depends. He holds a lasso color-coded to indicate the temperature and season in which it works best. As he watches the animals, Nils Peder is *yoiking,* chanting a throaty, traditional Sami song evoking his wife, Ingrid. The Lutheran pastors who converted the Sami forbade yoiking, calling it devil's music. When Nils Peder was a boy, his mother disapproved of it. He learned it from his grandparents and has taught it to his children. "When I yoik," says Nils Peder, who's also a fan of Johnny Cash, "I remember what I've seen, and I remember I am not alone."

NGM MAPS
SOURCE: LARS-ANDERS BAER, SAMI PARLIAMENT, SWEDEN

Mathis Gaup wades into the herd of pounding reindeer to separate
the pregnant cows—the ones that still have antlers—from the rest, briefly
grasping one reindeer by her hind leg to guide her outside the tarp-
enclosed stockade. In 2011 only 50 percent of the females bore calves

in the Gaup family's herds in Norway, down from the usual 80 percent.
Herders take bad years in stride. "Nature controls the size of the herd," says
Mathis's brother, Nils Peder. "Females that spend the summer caring only
for themselves can bear stronger calves the next spring."

Sven Skaltje makes a meal from some staples of the Sami diet—dried reindeer meat, homemade bread, coffee—in the kitchen of the apartment (right) he shares with five of his siblings in Gällivare, Sweden. They split their time between the town and their village of Harrå, unreachable by roads. Skaltje spends much of the winter on the tundra with his herd. "I feel empty when I am away from the reindeer," he says. A photo of a calf marking (above) hangs in his cousin's home.

A reindeer lies slaughtered on a table in the Gaups' modern kitchen in Kautokeino, Norway. Not a bit of it will go to waste. The family freezes, smokes, or dries the meat, as well as the organs, fat, blood, and even hooves. Some Sami make handicrafts using antlers and bones for tools and toys,

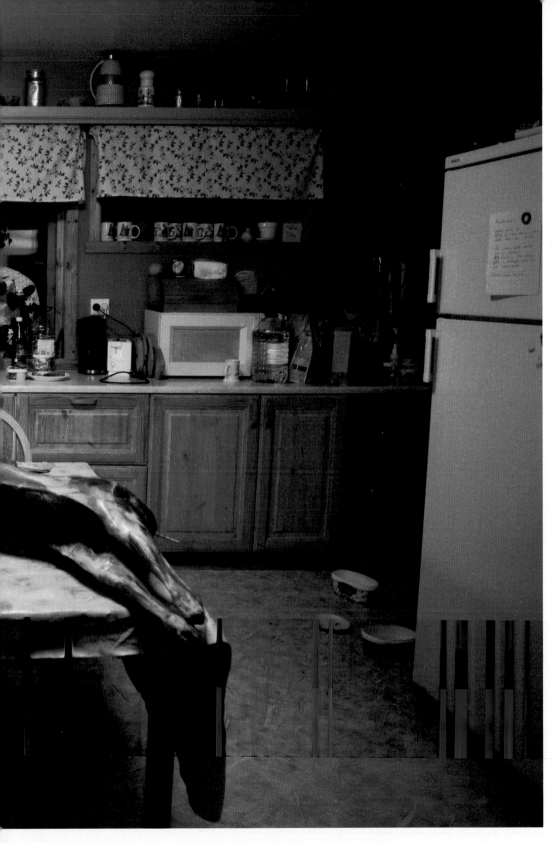

tendons for thread, and skins for bags and garments. They spend months preparing hides—scraping, soaking, drying, and stretching the leather by hand. To sell meat commercially, herders transport reindeer to slaughterhouses, which butcher the meat and discard the rest.

A stuffed reindeer decorates a grocery store in the town of Jokkmokk, Sweden. Ingrid Gaup (right) attended boarding school in Sweden before marrying and moving to Norway. She follows the Sami tradition of making some household items herself. She collects "shoe grass" in river marshes, dries and braids it, then shapes it to fit inside winter boots. "It traps warm air and absorbs moisture much better than modern insulation," says Ingrid.

Frames of cone-shaped tents called *lávut* are a common sight in Sami yards, where they are often used for smoking meat. Sami have long used the tents as portable shelters—their wide bases and forked poles enable them to withstand sustained winds of up to 50 miles an hour on the Arctic tundra. Easy to transport

and erect, the frames were originally covered with reindeer skins, but waxed canvas or lightweight woven materials are more common with today's herders, who use a fire or a stove at the center for warmth and cooking. Large families can sleep inside a single tent, protected from the cold ground by branches and reindeer hides.

Sven Skaltje was saddened to find the carcasses of two female reindeer whose antlers had become entangled during a dominance struggle in northern Sweden. He estimates it took three days for them to die of starvation. After separating the bodies, he saw from the unique ear markings that one belonged to him and the other to his cousin. Skaltje is much admired by the younger Sami in his herding group, but he is unsure whether the skills he teaches them will endure. "Other cultures, like the Romans and the Inca, were very important, and they disappeared," he says. "That is life."

Photographer Erika Larsen has been living with a Sami community in Kautokeino, Norway, since 2008 and documenting the lives of herders in Sweden as well. Read more of her story in The Moment, *page 160. Jessica Benko has written for* Virginia Quarterly Review *and* Harper's

RIFT
IN PARADISE

Africa's Albertine Rift

As the global population soars toward
nine billion by 2045, this corner of Africa
shows what's at stake in the decades ahead.
The Rift is rich in rainfall, deep lakes,
volcanic soil, and biodiversity. It is also one
of the most densely populated places on
Earth. A desperate competition
for land and resources—and
between people and wildlife—has
erupted here with unspeakable violence.
How can the conflict be stopped?
Will there be any room left for the wild?

A tree-climbing lion stirs in Uganda's Queen Elizabeth National Park.

Rule of the gun prevails in North Kivu, a conflict-ravaged province in the Democratic Republic of the Congo. The Mai-Mai Kifuafua, one of many local militias, flaunts its power on a road where it extorts money from villagers and travelers. For nearly 20 years near-constant fighting over land, mining riches, and power has terrorized the people.

PASCAL MAITRE

*Exhaling clouds of gas, a cauldron
of lava boils in the mile-wide crater of
Nyiragongo, an active volcano in
the Congo that threatens two million
people. Eruptions have blistered
the region for millions of years, since
the African tectonic plate began to
split apart to create the Albertine Rift.*

CARSTEN PETER

A metal-roofed metropolis, Goma sits at the crossroads of conflict in eastern Congo, its population exploding with displaced villagers, soldiers, profiteers, and aid workers. The lava-rumpled city sprawls between Lake Kivu, full of dangerous gases, and the restless Nyiragongo volcano.

PASCAL MAITRE

Elephants have miles of unbroken savanna to roam inside Uganda's Queen Elizabeth Park, where their numbers total 2,500, a dramatic rise after heavy poaching in the 1980s. Outside the preserve villagers kill elephants that trample and eat crops, though attacks have diminished with the digging of trenches to protect fields from wild trespassers.

JOEL SARTORE

A path from market to squatters' camp leads a woman carrying sugarcane across a recently burned plot in Uganda's Kagombe Forest Reserve. Desperate for land, 3,000 people live in the reserve, torching forest to clear plots for corn and other crops. Due to political pressure, rangers can't evict settlers, many of whom have nowhere else to go.

PASCAL MAITRE

The hand of a mountain gorilla
pokes from the rain forest in Bwindi
Impenetrable National Park in
Uganda. The number of endangered
primates has stabilized at some 780
in Bwindi and the Virunga Mountains
parks of Congo, Uganda, and Rwanda.

JOEL SARTORE

By **ROBERT DRAPER**

Photographs by **PASCAL MAITRE** *and* **JOEL SARTORE**

The mwami remembers when he was a king of sorts. His judgment was sovereign, his power unassailable. Since 1954 he, like his father and grandfather before him, has been the head of the Bashali chiefdom in the Masisi District, an undulating pastoral region in eastern Democratic Republic of the Congo (DRC). Though his name is Sylvestre Bashali Mokoto,

the other chiefs address him as simply doyen—seniormost. For much of his adult life, the mwami received newcomers to his district. They brought him livestock or other gifts. He in turn parceled out land as he saw fit.

Today the chief sits on a dirty couch in a squalid hovel in Goma, a Congolese city several hours south of Masisi. His domain is now the epicenter of a humanitarian crisis that has lasted for more than a decade yet has largely eluded the world's attention. Eastern Congo has been overtaken by thousands of Tutsi and Hutu and Hunde fighting over what they claim is their lawful property, by militias aiming to acquire land by force, by cattlemen searching for less cluttered pastures, by hordes of refugees from all over this fertile and dangerously overpopulated region of East Africa seeking somewhere, anywhere, to eke out a living. Some years ago a member of a rebel army seized the mwami's 200-acre estate, forcing him, humiliated and fearing for his safety, to retreat to this shack in Goma.

The city is a hornet's nest. As recently as two decades ago Goma's population was perhaps 50,000. Now it is at least 20 times that number. Armed males in uniform stalk its raggedy, unlit streets with no one to answer to. Streaming out of the outlying forests and into the city market is a 24/7 procession of people ferrying immense sacks of charcoal on bicycles or wooden, scooter-like *chukudus*. North of the city limits seethes Nyiragongo volcano, which last erupted in 2002, when its lava roared through town and wiped out Goma's commercial district. At the city's southern edge lies the silver cauldron of Lake Kivu—so choked with carbon dioxide and methane that some scientists predict a gas eruption in the lake could one day kill everyone in and around Goma.

The mwami, like so many far less privileged people, has run out of options. His stare is one of regal aloofness. Yet despite his cuff links and

SEVEN BILLION is a yearlong series on global population.

EUROPEAN EXPLORERS
CAME HERE SEARCHING
FOR THE SOURCE OF
THE NILE IN THE 19TH
CENTURY. EVEN THEN
THE PARADISE THAT
VISITORS BEHELD WAS
RACKED WITH A CENTRAL
PREOCCUPATION:
**IS THERE ENOUGH
FOR EVERYONE?**

trimmed gray beard, he is not a chief here in Goma. He is only Sylvestre Mokoto, a man swept into the hornet's nest, with no land left for him to parcel out. As his guest, a journalist from the West, I have brought no gifts, only demeaning questions. "Yes, of course my power has been affected greatly," the mwami snaps at me. "When others back up their claims with guns, there is nothing I can do."

The reign of the mwamis is finished in this corner of East Africa. The region has become a staging ground for violence of mind-reeling proportions over the past few decades: the murder and abduction of tens of thousands in northern Uganda, the massacre of more than a million in the genocides of Rwanda and Burundi, followed by two wars in eastern Congo, the last of which, known as the Great African war because so many neighboring countries were involved, is estimated to have killed more than five million people, largely through disease and starvation—the deadliest war since World War II. Armed conflicts that started in one country have seeped across borders and turned into proxy wars, with the region's governments each backing various rebel groups, a numbing jumble of acronymed militias—the LRA, FDLR, CNDP, RCD, AFDL, MLC, the list goes on—vying for power and resources

Robert Draper is a contributing writer for the magazine who reported on Afghanistan's opium crop in the February issue. He and photographer Pascal Maitre have collaborated on stories in Somalia and Madagascar. Joel Sartore frequently photographs wildlife for the magazine.

in one of the richest landscapes in all of Africa.

The horrific violence that has occurred in this place—and continues in lawless eastern Congo despite a 2009 peace accord—is impossible to understand in simple terms. But there is no doubt that geography has played a role. Erase the borders of Uganda, the DRC, Rwanda, Burundi, and Tanzania and you see what unites these disparate political entities: a landscape shaped by the violent forces of shifting plate tectonics. The East African Rift System bisects the horn of Africa—the Nubian plate to the west moving away from the Somalian plate to the east—before forking down either side of Uganda.

The western rift includes the Virunga and Rwenzori mountain ranges and several of Africa's Great Lakes, where the deep rift has filled with water. Called the Albertine Rift (after Lake Albert), this 920-mile-long geologic crease of highland forests, snowcapped mountains, savannas, chain of lakes, and wetlands is the most fecund and biodiverse region on the African continent, the home of gorillas, okapis, lions, hippos, and elephants, dozens of rare bird and fish species, not to mention a bounty of minerals ranging from gold and tin to the key microchip component known as coltan. In the 19th century European explorers like David Livingstone and John Hanning Speke came here searching for the source of the Nile. They gazed in awe at the profusion of lush vegetation and vast bodies of water, according to the scholar Jean-Pierre Chrétien: "In the heart of black Africa, the Great Lakes literally dazzled the whites."

The paradox of the Albertine Rift is that its very richness has led to scarcity. People crowded into this area because of its fertile volcanic soil, its plentiful rainfall, its biodiversity, and its high altitude, which made it inhospitable to mosquitoes and tsetse flies and the diseases they carry. As the population soared, more and more forest was cut down to increase farm and grazing land. Even in the 19th century the paradise that visitors beheld was already racked with a central preoccupation: Is there enough for everyone?

Today that question hangs over every square inch of the Albertine Rift, where the fertility rate is among the highest in the world, and where violence has erupted between humans and against animals—in a horror show of landgrabs, spastic waves of refugees, mass rapes, and plundered national parks, the last places on Earth where wildlife struggles to survive undisturbed by humans. For the impoverished residents of the region, overcrowding has spawned an anxiety so primal and omnipresent that one hears the same plea over and over again:

We want land!

The suspected lion killer sits near the shore of Lake George and plays a vigorous board game known as *omweso* with one of his fellow cattlemen. He looks up, introduces himself as Eirfazi Wanama, and says he cannot tell me his age or the number of his children. "We Africans don't count our offspring," he declares, "because you *muzungu* don't want us to produce so many children." Muzungu is slang for whites in this part of the world. Wanama offers a wry smile and says, "You don't have to beat about the bush. Some lions were killed here, and the rangers came in the middle of the night and arrested me."

In late May 2010 two rangers in Uganda's Queen Elizabeth National Park saw vultures hovering over a field in the park about a mile from Wanama's village of Hamukungu and discovered the dead bodies of five poisoned lions. Nearby were two cow carcasses that had been laced with a bluish pesticide called carbofuran. Early intelligence pointed to Wanama; another suspect fled the area. "They held me for a day," Wanama says. "They have released me from their investigation. I am not running away."

Hamukungu is located within the boundaries of the park, whose predominant tourist attraction is its population of lions, which has dwindled by about 40 percent in less than a decade. "The number of villagers has increased," says Wilson Kagoro, the park's community conservation warden, "as has the number of cattle. And this has created a big conflict between them and us. They sneak into the park late at night to let their cattle graze. When this happens, the lions feast on the cows." Given that parkland grazing is illegal, the aggrieved pastoralists are left with no legal recourse. But *(Continued on page 107)*

CHALLENGED REGION *Crowded and impoverished after decades of war and instability, Uganda, Rwanda, and the DRC rate near the bottom of every index of human development, which measure indicators such as life expectancy, literacy, and income.*

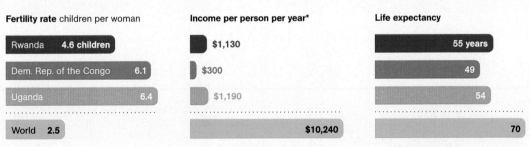

Fertility rate children per woman		Income per person per year*		Life expectancy	
Rwanda	4.6 children	$1,130			55 years
Dem. Rep. of the Congo	6.1	$300			49
Uganda	6.4	$1,190			54
World	2.5		$10,240		70

LATEST AVAILABLE DATA.   *GROSS NATIONAL INCOME PER CAPITA, PPP, IN 2009 U.S. DOLLARS
NGM ART. SOURCE: POPULATION REFERENCE BUREAU

SEES OF STRIFE

EARLY INHABITANTS

As far back as 6,000 B.C., hunter-gatherer communities lived on rivers feeding Lake Victoria.

1000 B.C.-A.D. 500 Bantu speakers from the west and Sudanic and Cushitic speakers from the north spread into the resource-rich region that is now Rwanda, Burundi, Uganda, and eastern Democratic Republic of the Congo (DRC). They bring iron and stone tools. By A.D. 500 these diverse peoples have merged into a single society and speak similar Bantu languages. They are both herders and farmers, growing sorghum, millet, and yams and raising cattle, sheep, and goats.

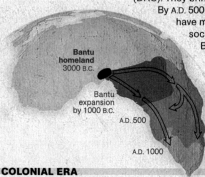

Bantu homeland 3000 B.C.

Bantu expansion by 1000 B.C.

A.D. 500

A.D. 1000

COLONIAL ERA

1919-1950s
After World War I, the Treaty of Versailles hands the German colony of Ruanda-Urundi to the Belgians, who give the Tutsi favored status, fueling divisions. Rwandan Hutu are brought to the Congo to work in mines and on plantations.

African colonies in 1911; from Keith Johnston's *General Atlas*
DAVID RUMSEY HISTORICAL MAP COLLECTION

Gunnery team, German East Africa
BARCH, BILD 105-DOA0151/WALTHER DOBBERTIN (ABOVE); TIME LIFE PICTURES/MANSELL/ GETTY IMAGES (RIGHT)

Leopold II, king of Belgium, ruled the Congo from 1885 to 1908.

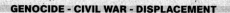

GENOCIDE - CIVIL WAR - DISPLACEMENT

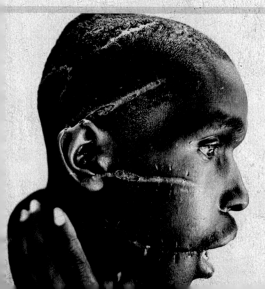

1993 The Hutu president of Burundi is assassinated, sparking a massacre of Tutsi. Around 700,000 people flee the country.

1994 Burundi's and Rwanda's presidents are killed in a suspicious plane crash, setting off a three-month rampage in Rwanda. About a million Tutsi and moderate Hutu are killed during the genocide, and more than two million flee, many into neighboring Zaire (now the DRC). Paul Kagame leads a Tutsi takeover of the Rwandan government, and Hutu militias retreat to eastern Zaire.

1996-97
(First Congo war) With Rwanda's and Uganda's help, Congolese Tutsi overthrow Zaire's dictator, Mobutu. Rebel leader Kabila becomes president of the renamed DRC.

Survivor of a Hutu death camp, Rwanda, 1994
JAMES NACHTWEY

Flag of Zaire, 1971-1997

The decades of violence in the Albertine Rift have been blamed on "ancient" ethnic rivalries, often viewed as endemic to the African continent. But underlying those divisions is a fierce competition for natural resources. For centuries a burgeoning population has stressed the environment's ability to provide enough for all, pitting herders against farmers, people against wildlife, brother against brother.

EXPLORATION

1600s
Highly organized monarchies expand throughout the region. Several kingdoms, such as Rwanda and Bunyoro, develop an elite class of cattle herders who separate themselves from the farmers by their dress and diet, becoming a distinct caste. Population growth leads to ecological pressure.

1800s
European explorers searching for the source of the Nile are astonished by the region's sophisticated kingdoms. They falsely assume an invading Nilotic people (like the Tutsi) subjugated the Bantu farmers (such as the Hutu). The ivory and slave trades flourish as European powers carve up Africa.

Sir Samuel Baker on Lake Albert, which he encountered in 1864.
PICTURE COLLECTION, NEW YORK PUBLIC LIBRARY

CREATION OF INDEPENDENT NATIONS

1925
Africa's first national park is founded to protect gorillas and their habitat in the Virunga Mountains from human encroachment.

Virunga National Park
JODY KURASH, AP IMAGES

RWANDA (1962, from Belgium)
UGANDA (1962, from U.K.)
DEM. REP. OF THE CONGO (1960, from Belgium)
BURUNDI (1962, from Belgium)
TANZANIA (1961/1963, from U.K.)

1960-62 Congo, Burundi, Rwanda, and Uganda gain independence. The small size of Rwanda and Burundi heightens tensions as the Tutsi and Hutu directly compete for power; ethnic tensions are diffused in the larger nations.

1972-73
Hutu rise up against the Tutsi-controlled government in Burundi. In response, Tutsi militias kill up to 200,000 Hutu, and an equal number flee to neighboring countries, mainly Tanzania. Throughout the region, the scarcity of land worsens ethnic disputes.

1986 Ugandan President Museveni comes to power. The rebel Lord's Resistance Army forms in northern Uganda; it goes on to kill or abduct tens of thousands.

1989 International trade in ivory is banned in response to the slaughter of Africa's elephants.

1998-2003
(Second Congo war) Congolese rebels backed by Rwanda and Uganda take control of eastern Congo. With outside help, Kabila pushes back the rebels; millions die.

Flag of the Democratic Republic of the Congo, 1997-2003

2006 Oil reserves are discovered at Lake Albert.

2007 Rangers in Virunga National Park find seven slaughtered mountain gorillas, bringing attention to the violence overtaking the park.

Villagers carry Senkwekwe, a gorilla killed in Virunga National Park, 2007.
BRENT STIRTON, REPORTAGE BY GETTY IMAGES

2010-present
Despite peace agreements, armed conflict continues in the resource-rich DRC. The ongoing tensions still pit ethnic groups against each other, but underlying the fighting are grievances over scarce land and conflict over mineral profits.

NGM STAFF

CROWDING OUT THE FOREST

One of the most densely populated rural regions of Africa, the Albertine Rift is also among the continent's richest biodiversity zones, creating competition between humans and wildlife alike. The western branch of Africa's Great Rift Valley extends for 920 miles, straddling the borders of multiple restive nations. Several of Africa's Great Lakes, among the deepest in the world, trace the Rift zone, a trough created by the fracturing of the Earth's crust.

AFRICA

RIFT SYSTEM

AREA DETAILED

SOUTH SUDAN

KENYA

UGANDA

DEMOCRATIC REPUBLIC OF THE CONGO

RWANDA

KIDEPO VALLEY N.P.

NIMULE N.P.

GARAMBA NAT. PARK

Albert Nile

Monts Bleus

Lake Albert

MURCHISON FALLS N.P.

Lake Kwania

Lake Kyoga

Victoria Nile

Mt. Elgon
14,177 ft
4,321 m

MT. ELGON NAT. PARK

EQUATOR

Kampala

Lake Victoria

N'DERE I. N.P.

RUMA N.P.

MASAI MARA NAT. RES.

Serengeti

Nansio

RUBONDO ISLAND N.P.

Bukoba

FERRY

Lake Ikimba

Lake Burigi

Lac Ihema

OKAPI FAUNAL RESERVE

CONGO BASIN

SEMULIKI N.P.

RWENZORI MTS. N.P.

Rwenzori Mts.

⌧ Kagombe Forest Reserve

KIBALE N.P.

Lake George

Hamukungu

QUEEN ELIZABETH NATIONAL PARK

LAKE MBURO N.P.

T. Nakivali

Lulimbi

Vitshumbi

Ishasha R.

Lake Edward

BWINDI IMPENETRABLE N.P.

MGAHINGA GORILLA N.P.

AKAGERA N.P.

Musanze (Ruhengeri)

VOLCANS N.P.

Kigali

Rwamagana

MAIKO N.P.

VIRUNGA NATIONAL PARK

Virunga Mts.

Volcan Nyiragongo

Goma

Lake Kivu

NORTH KIVU

MASISI

Masisi

Shasha

Minova

KAHUZI-BIEGA

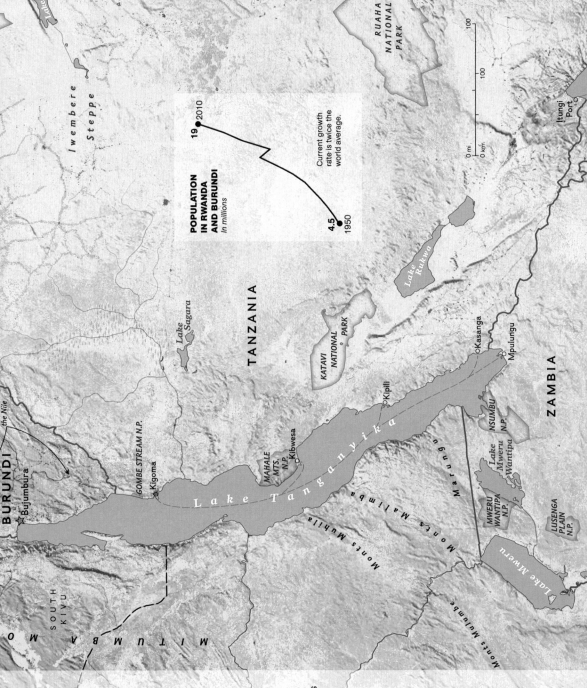

FOREST DEGRADATION
(1995-2006)

Practically the only highland forests left in the Rift survive in protected areas, which include dozens of parks and reserves. Conversion of forest to farmland was exacerbated by the wars of the 1990s, as huge numbers of displaced people cleared land. Parks are also losing forests because villagers use trees for charcoal. The Rift's western highlands descend into the Congo Basin, the largest tropical forest after the Amazon and rich in timber and minerals.

POPULATION DENSITY

People per sq km (sq mi)

200 (520) 1,000 (2,600)

Subsistence farmers crowd the fertile Rift zones. Some of the highest densities occur near the borders of protected areas, with settlers often spilling into parks and reserves. Land disputes have been at the root of much violence in the Rift, and with population growing, the region will likely stay combustible.

LAND COVER

Forest

Grassland

Bare Ground

POPULATION IN RWANDA AND BURUNDI
In millions

19 2010

Current growth rate is twice the world average.

4.5 1950

WILLIAM E. McNULTY, NGM STAFF

SOURCES: MATTHEW HANSEN AND PETER POTAPOV, SOUTH DAKOTA STATE UNIVERSITY: MODIS/TERRA VEGETATION CONTINUOUS FIELDS, NASA; OAK RIDGE NATIONAL LABORATORY LANDSCAN 2009

CHART SOURCE: UNITED NATIONS

Lake Kivu

Iwembere Steppe

RUAHA NATIONAL PARK

Itungi Port

BURUNDI

Bujumbura

Sources of the Nile

SOUTH KIVU

Lake Sagara

TANZANIA

GOMBE STREAM N.P.

Kigoma

Lake Tanganyika

Lake Rukwa

MAHALE MTS. N.P.

Kibwesa

Kipili

KATAVI NATIONAL PARK

Kasanga

Mpulungu

M I T U M B A   M O

Monts Muhila

Monts Mahimba

Monts Marungu

MWERU WANTIPA N.P.

NSUMBU N.P.

Lake Mweru Wantipa

ZAMBIA

LUSENGA PLAIN N.P.

Lake Mweru

0 mi
0 km.

From above, the scene is pastoral—
a lush blanket of fields in the highlands of northwest Rwanda. The
ground truth is grittier. Land is so
scarce in the crowded countryside
near Musanze that farmers struggle
to cultivate every foot of the steep,
eroding hillsides. Land pressures
set the stage for the 1994 genocide,
in which one million were killed.

PASCAL MAITRE

Direct from the forest, charcoal sells for $17 a bag at a lively market near Goma. Lacking electricity, almost every household in the region depends on charcoal for boiling water and cooking. Armed groups control the industry and have invaded Virunga National Park, where dozens of rangers have been killed trying to halt destruction of the forest.

CARSTEN PETER

Demand for food and fuel is stressing the region's resources. On the Uganda side of Lake Albert, where the fishing fleet has grown from 760 boats in the mid-1960s to almost 6,000, a boy nets only small species of fish (above), since the catch of big Nile perch and tilapia has plunged. Forests are thinning out too, as hardwood trees are turned into charcoal, filling the bags of men careering toward a Congo market.

(Continued from page 97) that does not mean that they are without countermeasures. "We are surviving on God's mercy," Wanama says when I ask how so many people manage to survive on so little land. "The creation of this national park has made us so poor! People have to live on the land!" It's a common complaint in the overcrowded villages that ring the region's networks of parks and reserves.

Queen Elizabeth Park was established in 1952 with the growing recognition that this region had the highest biomass of large mammals of anyplace on Earth, according to Andrew Plumptre, director of the Albertine Rift Programme of the Wildlife Conservation Society. But social and political upheaval made it difficult to protect the wildlife. Over the decades poachers and desperate villagers raided the parks and decimated the populations of elephants, hippos, and lions. By 1980 the number of elephants had dropped from 3,000 to 150 in Queen Elizabeth.

Virunga National Park in eastern Congo—Africa's oldest, founded in 1925—is among the most imperiled, with many people already settled inside its boundaries. The countryside, once teeming with charismatic megafauna, is eerily vacant. The park's tourist lodges are gutted. Since the Rwandan genocide of 1994, much of the park has been closed to tourists.

The park is a war zone. Rodrigue Mugaruka is the warden of Virunga's central sector, Rwindi. He is a former child soldier who participated in the 1997 overthrow of Mobutu Sese Seko, the longtime dictator of the DRC (then called Zaire). In eastern Congo the vacuum created by Mobutu's exit led to fierce competition among proxy armies and various militias for its gold, charcoal, tin, and coltan. Now Mugaruka is doing battle with militias—called Mai-Mai fighters—who control illegal fishing and charcoal production in many of the villages that have cropped up inside the park on the western shore of Lake Edward. He recently regained control of his sector from thousands of Congolese soldiers stationed there to fight off the militias. Since the government rarely paid the soldiers, they resorted to killing the wildlife for food.

Mugaruka's efforts to enforce park regulations do not sit well with the tens of thousands of Congolese who have fled areas of conflict and taken up residence in the villages. In the fishing hamlet of Vitshumbi the warden orders park rangers to chop up, douse in kerosene, and set fire to several unlicensed fishing boats, illegal nets, and bags of charcoal, while the villagers look on bitterly. In a fishing boat dented from gunfire he ferries us to Lulimbi village, from which we drive to the Ishasha River bordering Uganda, where 96 percent of the park's hippo population has been slaughtered since 1976 and sold for bush meat by militias. Later we head to the park's Mount Tshiaberimu subsector, where an armed patrol provides round-the-clock protection to 15 eastern lowland gorillas from militias and from villagers who have been encouraged by politicians to claim parkland.

Rodrigue Mugaruka knows that he's a marked man. The Mai-Mai—and the Congolese businessmen who fund them—have made him a target. "Their objective is to chase us out of the park for good," says the warden. "When we seize a boat and a net, the businessmen tell the Mai-Mai, 'Before we put another net in the water, you must go kill a ranger.' Three of mine have been killed in the lake. If you consider the whole area, more than 20 rangers have been killed."

Last January, Mugaruka's men were ambushed with a rocket-propelled grenade by militia fighters along a road that goes through the center of the park. Three rangers and five Congolese soldiers were killed. Government officials soon received a petition signed by 100,000 villagers demanding that Virunga National Park be reduced in size by nearly 90 percent. The petitioners gave the government three months to release the land, which they claimed belonged to them. After that, warned the petition, the villagers would all grow crops in the park—and defend their activities with arms.

"We want land!"

The speaker gives his name as Charles, a 24-year-old sitting on a freshly cut log in a forest, a machete in his hand. He does not belong here, in Uganda's Kagombe Forest Reserve. Then again, maybe he does. No less than a presidential order has stopped the evictions of those who've encroached on forest reserves and wetlands. Charles says a government minister recently visited the Kagombe inhabitants. "He told us we can stay," he says, grinning. The minister's cronies have an election coming up, and the best way to placate voters is to promise them land.

Charles and a few other pioneering young

villagers moved into the forest in 2006. "We'd been living on our grandparents' property, but there were too many people on the land already," he says. "We heard people talk about how there was free land this way." A migrant group, the Bakiga, had already begun to settle in Kagombe, and when the National Forestry Authority tried to evict them, Uganda's President Yoweri Museveni—himself facing reelection—issued the executive order forbidding evictions. Thereupon a few local politicians urged the native Banyoro people, who include Charles and his friends, to grab some forestland as well, lest all of Kagombe wind up inhabited by nonlocals.

Charles and his friends each claimed about seven acres of timberland and began slashing away. They built grass-thatched huts, feed-storage sheds, a road, and a church. They planted corn, bananas, cassava, and Irish potatoes. Then they sent for their wives and began to have more children. Today Charles is one of about 3,000 inhabitants of the forest reserve and has no desire to leave. "We're very well off here," he says.

The forest, meanwhile, sometimes looks like a smoky wasteland, as people use fire to clear the forest for crops. The damage goes beyond the aesthetic: Kagombe serves as one of a series of connective forests that make up a wildlife corridor for chimps and other animals. As Sarah Prinsloo of the Wildlife Conservation Society observes, "The health of the wildlife population in these parks is dependent on corridors like Kagombe." The habitat destruction has contributed to a plunging animal population throughout the region. In Kagombe itself most wildlife has been hunted out.

The forestry authority's sector manager, Patrick Kakeeto, contemplates the devastation with a despairing smile. "They're cutting all of this down," he says. "And we can't touch them. For us, it's a kind of psychoprofessional torture."

How did this land of plenty descend into a perilous free-for-all? Dig deep into its history and it turns out the Albertine Rift has been shaped by mistaken ideas about its ethnic identities. The archaeological and linguistic evidence indicates that by as early as A.D. 500 various peoples had migrated into the region and forged a heterogeneous society that spoke similar Bantu languages and supported itself with both farming and herding. In the 15th century centralized kingdoms such as Bunyoro and Rwanda arose, along with exclusive classes of pastoralists, who distinguished themselves from farmers by their dress and a diet of milk, meat, and blood. Over time these pastoralists became distinct from the rest of the population, and their influence grew.

By the time European explorer John Hanning Speke arrived in the late 19th century, he was astonished by the highly organized kingdoms he encountered, complete with courts and diplomats. He assumed the elite pastoralists, known as Hima or Tutsi, were a superior race of Nilotic people (from what is now Ethiopia) who had invaded the Great Lakes and subjugated what he regarded as the lowly indigenous Bantu farmers, such as Iru or Hutu. "The states of the Great Lakes challenged derogatory racial beliefs about African intellect and ability," says archaeologist Andrew Reid. The idea of a Nilotic invasion was a way to explain away the existence of sophisticated kingdoms in the heart of Africa. The only problem: It wasn't true.

That didn't stop the Tutsi and other elites from embracing the story of their exotic origins to better differentiate themselves from the majority Hutu. And after East Africa was divided between European powers in the late 19th century, the Germans and then the Belgians were only too happy to co-opt what appeared to be the natural social hierarchy and give preference to what they believed to be the superior minority of Tutsi.

Despite the oft-cited physical differences between the two groups—the Tutsi are supposed to be taller, lighter skinned, and thinner lipped than the Hutu—it was so difficult to tell the two apart that by 1933 the Belgians had resorted to issuing identity cards: The 15 percent who owned cattle or had certain physical features were defined as Tutsi, and the rest were Hutu. (Members of one family sometimes ended up in different groups.) These identity cards, officially codifying a caste system that separated one people into two, would be used during the Rwanda genocide to single out who would live and who would be murdered. By the time the colonizers granted the countries independence in the early 1960s, ethnic hostilities between Tutsi and Hutu had already led to waves of killings and retaliatory murders. Today tensions between these two groups continue to play out in the Congo.

But clearly the Rwanda genocide was the result of more than Hutu-Tutsi ethnic hatred. The latter years of the 20th century had brought a sobering recognition that there was in fact not enough for everyone in the Albertine Rift—and with that, catastrophe. An alarming rise in population coincided with a slump in coffee and tea prices in the 1980s, leading to great deprivation; poverty led to an even greater strain on the land. Although it's true that a country like the Netherlands had a population density as high as Rwanda did at this time, it also benefited from mechanized, high-yield agriculture. Rwanda's dependence on traditional subsistence farming meant that the only way to grow more food was to move onto ever more marginal land.

By the mid-1980s every acre of arable land outside the parks was being farmed. Sons were inheriting increasingly smaller plots of land, if any at all. Soils were depleted. Tensions were high. Belgian economists Catherine André and Jean-Philippe Platteau conducted a study of land disputes in one region in Rwanda before the genocide and found that more and more households were struggling to feed themselves on little land. Interviewing residents after the genocide, the researchers found it was not uncommon to hear Rwandans argue that "war is necessary to wipe out an excess of population and to bring numbers into line with the available land resources." Thomas Malthus, the famed English economist who posited that population growth would outstrip the planet's ability to sustain it unless kept in check by starvation, disease, or war, couldn't have put it more succinctly.

André and Platteau do not suggest that the genocide was an inevitable outcome of population

RWANDA'S GENOCIDE WAS INSTIGATED BY THE DECISIONS OF POWER-HUNGRY POLITICIANS. BUT A SCARCITY OF LAND SET THE STAGE FOR THE MASS KILLING. IN SHORT, THE GENOCIDE GAVE LANDLESS HUTU THE COVER THEY NEEDED TO INITIATE CLASS WARFARE.

pressures, since the killings were clearly instigated by the decisions of power-hungry politicians. But several scholars, including French historian Gérard Prunier, are convinced that a scarcity of land set the stage for the mass killing. In short, the genocide gave landless Hutu the cover they needed to initiate class warfare. "At least part of the reason why it was carried out so thoroughly by the ordinary rank-and-file peasants...was the feeling that there were too many people on too little land," Prunier observed in *The Rwanda Crisis,* "and that with a reduction in their numbers, there would be more for the survivors."

The eastern Congo village of Shasha has become a grim crossroads between major destinations in North Kivu for armed groups seeking land, minerals, and revenge. Mines holding eastern Congo's abundant tin, coltan, and gold are almost exclusively under the control of these roving bands—Hutu and Tutsi paramilitaries, Mai-Mai militias, army soldiers—each descending on Shasha in a macabre rotation, one after another, month after month, in a wave of mayhem.

A woman named Faida weeps quietly as she recalls what happened to her a year ago. She is petite, with fatigued eyes and a voice just above a whisper. In her hands is a letter from her husband, demanding that she leave their house because he feared she might have contracted HIV from the men who raped her.

On that fateful day Faida was on the same road she always took after working in the

Attacked in their homes and fields, impregnated, and often cast off by their families, shattered women bring their babies to meet an aid worker in Shasha in North Kivu, a province terrorized by what activists call Congo's epidemic of rape as a weapon of war. Soldiers and rebels moving through the area have raped more than 800 women in this village alone.

PASCAL MAITRE

peanut fields. She would walk an hour and a half to the market at Minova with the peanuts on her back, then return home with firewood. Faida was 32 and of the Hunde ethnic group, married with six children, and for 16 years this had been her routine. She believed no one would attack a woman in broad daylight.

The three men were rebel Hutu. She tried to run, but the load on her back was heavy. The men told her to choose between life and death. Then they dragged her into a cattle field. She lost consciousness.

Today she and her children live with neighbors, and she cannot work. Her husband took another wife. The physical damage done is extensive. "I'm really suffering," she says. "Please help me with medicine, I beg you."

Shasha's population is about 10,000, twice what it was in 1994, and its story is, writ small, that of eastern Congo. A Hunde stronghold since antiquity, Shasha saw an influx of Hutu in the 1930s, when the Belgian occupiers brought them in to work their plantations. Later, in the wake of the 1994 genocide, thousands more Hutu came as refugees. Land disputes became overheated and were frequently resolved at the point of a gun. The area's vast mineral wealth only made things worse. Scarcity and abundance exist here side by side, fueling grievances as well as greed, both spiraling into inexplicable violence against innocents.

Goma women's advocate Marie Gorette estimates that more than 800 females in the village have been raped. They ranged in age, she says, from nine months to 80. One afternoon we sit in a hut while women enter one by one to tell their stories. Odette is strong shouldered and wears a blue print dress. It happened to her just ten days ago. Her 12-year-old son found her unconscious in the cassava fields where she had been working. Justine looks much younger than 28 and has lively eyes. The Congolese Tutsi warlord Laurent Nkunda (under house arrest in Rwanda since 2009) sent CNDP troops into Shasha in 2008. Justine was far from the only one—many of her relatives and neighbors were raped as well. Another woman, 42, tells how Congolese Tutsi

rebels barged into her house four years ago, took all the family's money, and raped her. "It's a secret," she says, and I sadly realize she's told me her story only because she thinks I can help her.

Some 200,000 females in the Congo were raped between 1996 and 2008, and more than 8,000 in the eastern provinces of North Kivu and South Kivu in 2009 alone. And despite international attention following a 2009 visit to the region by U.S. Secretary of State Hillary Rodham Clinton, the rapes continue. Just as the "Hutu power" Rwandans sought to eradicate the Tutsi in 1994 by massacring women and children, Shasha's invaders are human heat-seeking missiles aimed at the village's women. "Because it's the corridor, Shasha is the worst place in the region when it comes to mass rapes," says Gorette. "They use rape as a weapon to destroy a generation."

I am somewhere in Rwanda when my car breaks down. A man pulls over to where I'm hovering over the smoking engine and offers to drive me the remaining 70 or so miles to Kigali. "If this were the Congo, you would be in big trouble," he says laughing.

The 41-year-old man's name is Samuel, and though he is from the farming community of Rwamagana, his vocation is carpentry. By the region's standards, Samuel's family is small. "Only four children," he says. "I think that's the ideal size." Schools cost Samuel about $650 per child each term. "But I think education is the solution. Otherwise people have no work. They just resort to having lots of children and stealing to survive." The broad-faced man smiles and says, "I'm very optimistic about our country. The future is indeed bright."

It is no small miracle that the country where the Albertine Rift's anxieties and resentments metastasized into genocide would, less than two decades later, emerge as the region's beacon of hope. Rwanda's President Paul Kagame drove out the Hutu leaders of the massacre and helped set up a Tutsi regime that has been in power ever since. While many credit Kagame with bringing stability and economic growth to this troubled region, several historians have come to view his regime as a repressive autocracy that favors the Tutsi minority. He's come under harsh criticism for human rights abuses against dissidents and for using paramilitary groups to divert mineral riches from eastern Congo to Rwanda. Though Rwanda has largely stopped the direct plunder of resources that occurred during and after Congo's last war, Kagame's plans to build up his country undoubtedly depend on covertly exploiting Congo's mineral wealth.

Still, there's no denying the long list of successes Kagame has piled up in an incredibly impoverished place. Rwanda is now one of the safest and most stable countries in this part of Africa. The roads are paved, the landscape is tidy, and the government has launched an ambitious campaign to preserve what little forest is left in Rwanda. Government programs train poachers for alternative livelihoods. An event known as Kwita Izina has raised awareness of wildlife conservation with an annual ceremony to name every newborn mountain gorilla in Rwanda. A law passed this past June provides compensation for any livestock—or humans—hurt or killed by wildlife. And hundreds of thousands of acres owned by wealthy landowners in the country's Eastern Province were shrewdly redistributed to citizens in 2008, before Kagame's reelection—though the president and other influential cronies continue to own sprawling estates.

Unlike Uganda, where President Museveni has declared its high fertility rate a tool in building a productive workforce, Rwanda is tackling its high fertility rate with aggressive family planning. "When I look at the problem of Rwanda's population, it starts with the high fertility rate among our poor women. And this impacts everything—the environment, the relationship between our people, and the country's development in general," says Jean-Damascène Ntawukuliryayo, the deputy speaker of parliament. "For all the visible progress Rwanda is making, if we don't address this matter, then it will create a bottleneck, and our development will be unsustainable."

Yet even if Rwanda's fertility rate falls below replacement level, as it's projected to do by 2050,

TO FEED ITS BURGEONING POPULATION AND PROTECT WILDLIFE, RWANDA WILL NEED TO PRODUCE MUCH MORE FOOD ON MUCH LESS LAND —A TALL ORDER IN THIS PART OF THE WORLD. EVEN KAGAME'S STRONG-MAN GOVERNMENT CAN ONLY DO SO MUCH.

its population will still triple beyond what it was before the 1994 genocide. Forty-three percent of Rwandans are under the age of 15; 30 percent are illiterate; 81 percent live in rural areas. To feed its burgeoning population and protect the wildlife still left in its parks, Rwanda will need to figure out how to produce much more food on much less land—a tall order in this part of the world. Even Kagame's strongman government can do only so much so fast.

"The average family of six has little more than half an acre here," says Pierre Rwanyindo Ruzirabwoba, director of Rwanda's Institute of Research and Dialogue for Peace. "And of course those children will have children. Where will they grow crops? That small piece of land has been overworked and is no longer fertile. I'm afraid another war could be around the corner."

Another full-scale war in the heart of the Albertine Rift? It's an awful thing to contemplate. Ruzirabwoba fretfully ponders the way out. High-yield farming techniques, of course. Better job opportunities in the city. And "a good relationship with our neighboring countries."

Then he shrugs and says, "Perhaps some of our people can migrate to the Congo." □

SEVEN BILLION IN DECEMBER
With nine billion people on Earth by 2045, cities will explode. How can we make them livable—and lovable?

The Pulitzer Center on Crisis Reporting and PBS NewsHour *join us in reporting on population issues throughout the year.*

The magazine thanks the David and Lucile Packard Foundation, the Wallace Global Fund, and National Geographic Society members for their generous support.

In a region bursting with people, a few big open spaces remain—like the Rift floor in Queen Elizabeth Park, pocked with crater lakes formed by volcanic explosions. If protected areas hadn't been set aside in the Albertine Rift from the 1920s to the 1960s, conservationists doubt any large wilderness areas would exist today.

JOEL SARTORE

Alert to human visitors, a young mountain gorilla and its mother sit tight in Bwindi Impenetrable Park. When the park opened in 1991, villagers resented losing access to forest where they had gathered honey and wood. Today the park shares the fees from gorilla-watching tours with the locals, a small victory in the Rift's unending clashes for livable space.

JOEL SARTORE

THERE WAS ONLY ONE WAY SCIENTISTS COULD UNLOCK THE MYSTERY OF THE FAMOUS ICEMAN. TAKE AWAY HIS ICE.

THE ICEMAN'S ARM THAWS ON A SHEET OF STERILIZED FOIL.

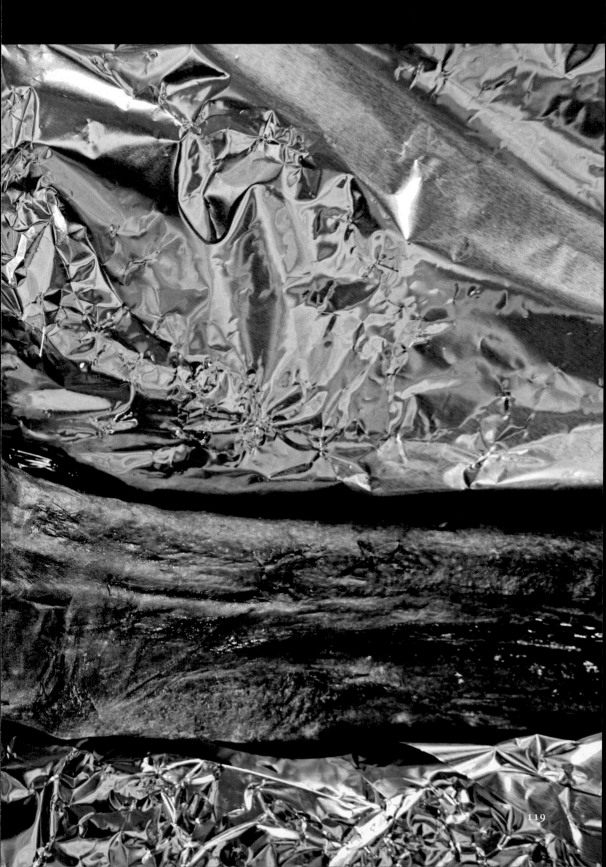

HIS JOURNEY
BEGAN ON A
SPRING DAY 5,300
YEARS AGO.

Dutch artists Adrie and Alfons Kennis used 3-D scans of the Iceman's skeleton and other anatomical clues to create a life-size model (left). Scientists once believed he had blue eyes; his DNA now proves they were brown. On his last trek he wore hay-and-hide shoes (above, on glass model) held together with bark fibers.

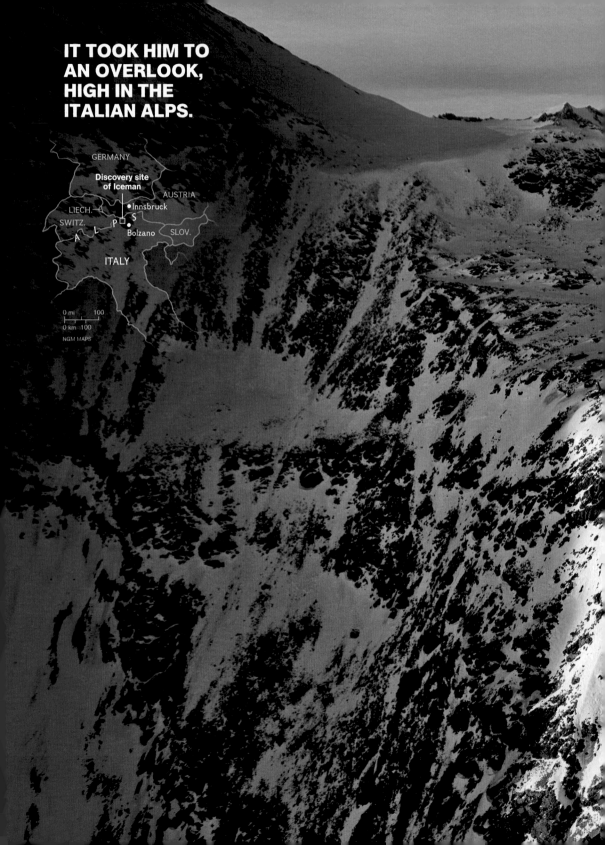

IT TOOK HIM TO
AN OVERLOOK,
HIGH IN THE
ITALIAN ALPS.

GERMANY

**Discovery site
of Iceman**

AUSTRIA

• Innsbruck

LIECH.

SWITZ.   S
          P □
        • Bolzano   SLOV.

A   L

ITALY

0 mi   100
0 km   100
NGM MAPS

The arrow shows where hikers discovered the Iceman's body in 1991, poking out of glacial ice in a shallow bowl of rock at an altitude of about 10,500 feet. A rich assortment of Neolithic artifacts were scattered around the body. The site, in the Italian part of the Ötztal Alps, gave rise to the mummy's nickname: Ötzi.

HE DID NOT KNOW THE MEAL HE ATE WOULD BE HIS LAST.

1 Overlooking the Senales Valley, the Iceman paused to enjoy a greasy repast of ibex and grain—and a false sense of calm.

2 Shortly after the meal, an assassin fired a fatal arrow into his back.

3 The assassin may have delivered a final blow to the head.

4 The Iceman's killer likely retrieved the shaft of his arrow—it could have betrayed his identity—and fled.

BY STEPHEN S. HALL
PHOTOGRAPHS BY ROBERT CLARK

Shortly after 6 p.m. on a drizzling, dreary November day in 2010, two men dressed in green surgical scrubs opened the door of the Iceman's chamber in the South Tyrol Museum of Archaeology in Bolzano, Italy. They slid the frozen body onto a stainless steel gurney. One of the men was a young scientist named Marco Samadelli. Normally, it was his job to keep the famous Neolithic mummy frozen under the precise conditions that had preserved it for 5,300 years, following an attack that had left the Iceman dead, high on a nearby mountain. On this day, however, Samadelli had raised the temperature in the museum's tiny laboratory room to 18°C—64°F.

With Samadelli was a local pathologist with a trim mustache named Eduard Egarter Vigl, known informally as the Iceman's "family doctor." While

Stephen S. Hall last visited the Iceman in the July 2007 issue of the magazine. Robert Clark is a frequent contributor. His most recent story, "The Genius of the Inca," appeared in April 2011.

Egarter Vigl poked and prodded the body with knowing, sometimes brusque familiarity, a handful of other scientists and doctors gathered around in the cramped space, preparing to do the unthinkable: defrost the Iceman. The next day, in a burst of hurried surgical interventions as urgent as any operation on a living person, they would perform the first full-scale autopsy on the thawed body, hoping to shed new light on the mystery of who the Iceman really was and how he had died such a violent death.

Egarter Vigl and Samadelli carefully transferred

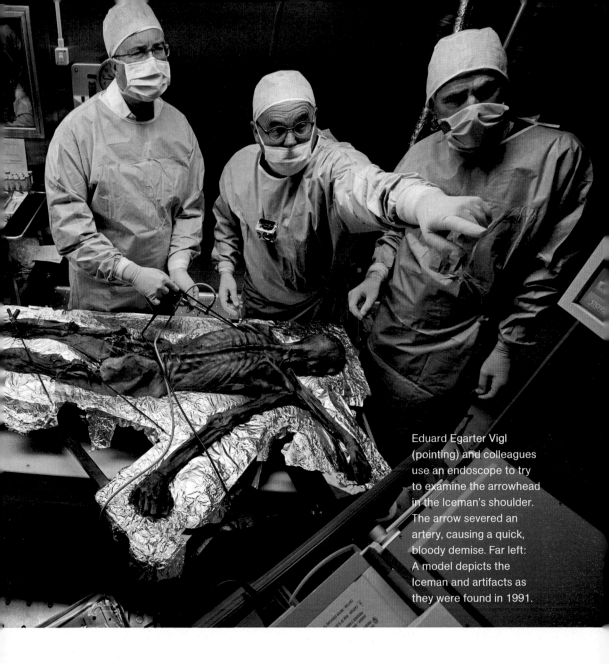

Eduard Egarter Vigl (pointing) and colleagues use an endoscope to try to examine the arrowhead in the Iceman's shoulder. The arrow severed an artery, causing a quick, bloody demise. Far left: A model depicts the Iceman and artifacts as they were found in 1991.

the body to a custom-made box lined with sterilized aluminum foil. In its frozen state, the Iceman's deep caramel skin had a dignified luster, reminiscent of a medieval figure painted in egg tempera. With the agonized reach of his rigid left arm and the crucifixate tilt of his crossed feet, the defrosting mummy struck a pose that wouldn't look out of place in a 14th-century altarpiece. Within moments, beads of water, like anxious sweat, began to form on his body. One droplet trickled down his chin with the slow inevitability of a tear.

THIS WAS NOT the first time that the Iceman had been subject to intense scientific scrutiny. After Austrian authorities first recovered the mummy in 1991, scientists in Innsbruck cut a large gash across his lower torso as part of their initial investigation, along with other incisions in his back, at the top of the skull, and on his legs. It was later determined that the shallow conch of gray rock where he had been found was on the Italian side of the border with Austria, so the body and the artifacts surrounding it were relocated to Bolzano. Over the years, numerous

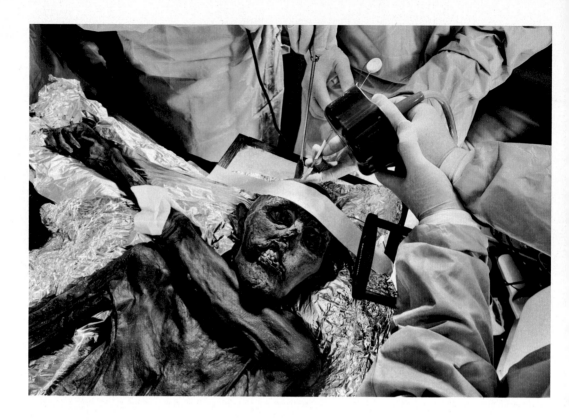

less invasive explorations of the remains were conducted there, including x-ray and CT scan imaging studies and an analysis of the mummy's mitochondrial DNA. The most astonishing revelation came in 2001, when a local radiologist named Paul Gostner noticed a detail that had been overlooked in the images: an arrowhead buried in the Iceman's left shoulder, indicating that he had been shot from behind. Later work by Gostner and his colleagues with more powerful CT imaging devices revealed that the arrow had pierced a major artery in the thoracic cavity, causing a hemorrhage that would have been almost immediately fatal. The oldest accidentally preserved human ever found was the victim of a brutally efficient murder.

Other scientists filled in biographical details. Analysis of chemical traces in his bones and teeth indicated that Ötzi, as he is also called, grew up northeast of Bolzano, possibly in the Isarco River Valley, and spent his adulthood in the

■ **Society Grant** The Iceman's autopsy was funded in part by your National Geographic Society membership.

Venosta Valley. Pollen found in his body placed his final hours in the springtime, and his last hike probably along a path up the Senales Valley toward an alpine pass just west of the Similaun Glacier. Close examination of his hand revealed a partially healed injury, suggestive of a defensive wound from an earlier fight. DNA analysis of food remnants found in his intestines—his stomach appeared to be empty—indicated that sometime before he met his demise, he had eaten red meat and some sort of wheat. Putting these facts together, scientists theorized that adversaries had an altercation with the Iceman in the valley south of the pass, chased him, and caught up with him on the mountain, where the body was discovered more than 5,000 years later.

It was a good story that fit the evidence—until Gostner took a closer look at the Iceman's guts. Though he had retired, the radiologist kept studying the CT scans at home as a kind of hobby, and in 2009 he became convinced that scientists had mistaken the Iceman's empty colon for his stomach, which had been pushed up under

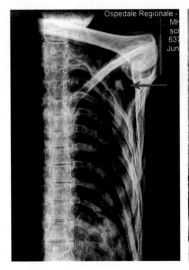

THE AUTOPSY

Probing and snipping for nine hours, scientists harvested dozens of biological clues about the life—and death—of the Iceman. Neurosurgeons retrieved bits of a blood clot (opposite), suggesting brain trauma around the time he died. X-rays guided the team in their attempt to find the fatal arrowhead (above left). The cross tattoo near the knee may have been a folk remedy for arthritic joint pain. Remnants of the Iceman's stomach and last meal (in test tubes) prompted one doctor to say, "He had a good appetite!"

his rib cage and appeared to Gostner to be full. If he was right, it meant the Iceman had eaten a large, and presumably leisurely, meal minutes before his death—not the sort of thing someone being chased by armed enemies would likely do.

"Gostner came over and told us he thought the stomach was full," said Albert Zink, director of the EURAC Institute for Mummies and the Iceman in Bolzano, who oversaw the autopsy last November. "And we thought, OK, then we have to go inside and sample the stomach." After further thought, Zink and his colleagues drew up a more ambitious plan: a head-to-toe investigation involving seven separate teams of surgeons, pathologists, microbiologists, and technicians. Perhaps most remarkable, this choreographed intervention would be accomplished without making any new incisions in the Iceman's body. Instead, the scientists would enter the body through the "Austrian windows"— their name for the overenthusiastic cuts made by the initial investigators.

"This will happen once," Zink said, "and then never again for many, many years."

"THIS IS THE BRAIN," announced neurosurgeon Andreas Schwarz, as he maneuvered a neurological endoscope into the top of the Iceman's head. Like the other scientists in the room, Schwarz was wearing 3-D glasses, and as he inched the instrument deeper inside the skull, a blurry 3-D image appeared on a computer monitor. It was a little after 1 p.m., and by that point the Iceman had already undergone six hours of poking, probing, gouging, and sample gathering. The surgical teams had taken snippets of muscle and lung. They had bored a hole in his pelvis to collect bone tissue for DNA analysis. They had rummaged around his thorax, trying to get close to the arrowhead and the tissue around it. They had even plucked some of his pubic hair. His skin had lost its luster and had a dull, leathery look, like a chicken wing left in the freezer too long.

Now they were peeking inside his brain to see if a mysterious shadow on a previous CT image might be an internal clot, or hematoma, at the rear of the skull, indicating a blow to the head. But the operation was not going

THE ARTIFACTS

His possessions bring the Iceman—and his era—to life. Two chunks of birch fungus on leather straps (left), possibly used to stanch bleeding and prevent infection, were part of a portable first aid kit. The flint-bladed dagger (above left) and two arrows (above right) served for hunting and self-defense. The ax with a blade of rare copper (center) marked him as a man of status. A maple leaf (right) in his pack was used to wrap embers; its chlorophyll content indicates the leaf was picked when green. His shoes—hay for warmth inside deerskin uppers with bearskin sole (below)—are among the oldest ever found. The tangle of string (below right), possibly his bowstring, remains a knotty mystery.

smoothly. Schwarz's endoscope kept bumping into ice crystals that blurred the camera lens. After an hour, the neurosurgery team finished up, not entirely sure whether they had obtained a viable sample.

The initial attempts to explore the stomach were also frustrating. Peter Malfertheiner, of the Otto-von-Guericke University of Magdeburg, tried to insinuate an endoscope down the Iceman's throat into the stomach, but five millennia of atrophy and mummification blocked the way. Egarter Vigl stepped in with a less delicate approach. Using the large Austrian window at the lower end of the torso, he stuck a gloved hand into the Iceman's gut. He pulled out two large chunks of undigested food, then switched to a kitchen spoon and scooped several more ounces from the Iceman's very full stomach.

By the end of the day, the laboratory freezer brimmed with 149 biological samples—"enough for about 50 papers," quipped one of the biologists. As soon as the autopsy concluded, Samadelli lowered the temperature in the laboratory below freezing. The next morning he and Egarter Vigl spruced up the body with a fine spray of sterilized water, which froze on contact. Then they slid the Iceman back into his high-tech igloo and closed the door.

THE AUTOPSY HAD TAKEN about nine hours; analysis of the material gleaned will take years. The first revelations were disclosed in June, when Zink and his colleagues presented some of their initial findings at a scientific meeting. Thanks to the DNA in a tiny speck of pelvic bone culled during the autopsy, the Iceman has joined the company of renowned biologists James D. Watson and J. Craig Venter as one of a handful of humans whose genomes have been sequenced in exquisite detail.

The genetic results add both information and intrigue. From his genes, we now know that the Iceman had brown hair and brown eyes and that he was probably lactose intolerant and thus could not digest milk—somewhat ironic, given theories that he was a shepherd. Not surprisingly, he is more related to people living in southern Europe today than to those in North Africa or the Middle East, with close connections to geographically isolated modern populations in Sardinia, Sicily, and the Iberian Peninsula. The DNA analysis also revealed several genetic variants that placed the Iceman at high risk for hardening of the arteries. ("If he hadn't been shot," Zink remarked, "he probably would have died of a heart attack or stroke in ten years.") Perhaps most surprising, researchers found the genetic footprint of bacteria known as *Borrelia burgdorferi* in his DNA—making the Iceman the earliest known human infected by the bug that causes Lyme disease.

The autopsy results have also rewritten the story of the Iceman's final moments. The neuroscientists determined that blood had indeed accumulated at the back of the Iceman's brain, suggesting some sort of trauma—either from falling on his face from the force of the arrow, Zink speculated, or perhaps from a coup de grâce administered by his assailant. DNA analysis of the final meal is ongoing, but one thing is already clear: It was greasy. Initial tests indicate the presence of fatty, baconlike meat of a kind of wild goat called an alpine ibex. "He really must have had a heavy meal at the end," Zink said—a fact that undermines the notion that he was fleeing in fear. Instead, it appears he was resting in a spot protected from the wind, tranquilly digesting his meal, unaware of the danger he was in.

And of course, unaware of the intense attention awaiting him far in the future. The Iceman might be the most exposed and invaded person who ever walked the planet. "There were moments yesterday," Zink said in a soft, almost surprised voice, "when you felt sorry for him. He was so…*explored*. All his secrets—inside him, outside him, all around him—were open to exploration." He paused and added, "Only the arrowhead remains inside him, as if he's saying, This is my last secret." □

NOVΛ | ☐ NATIONAL GEOGRAPHIC

Iceman Murder Mystery, a new NOVA–National Geographic Special, airs Wednesday, October 26, on PBS; check local listings.

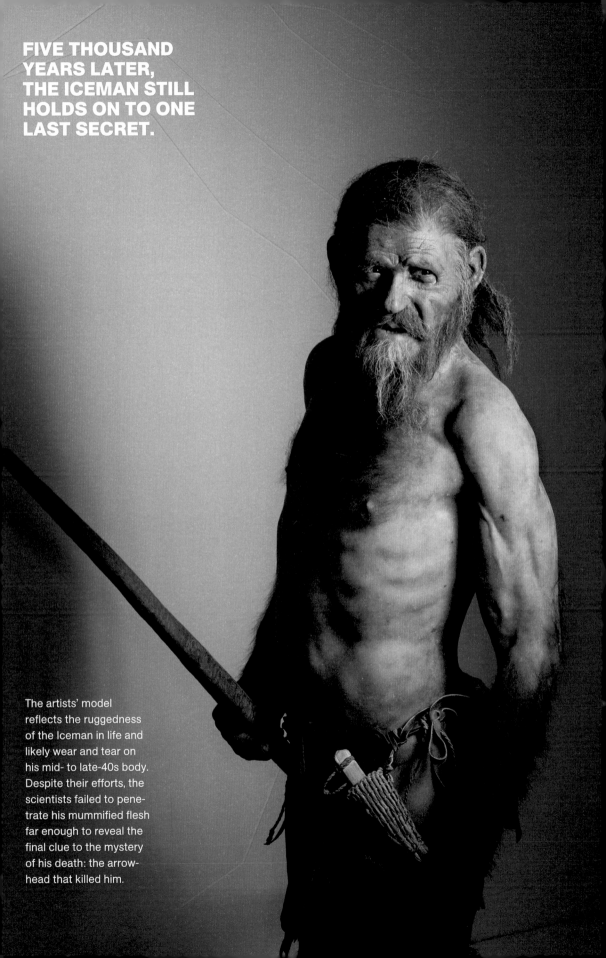

FIVE THOUSAND YEARS LATER, THE ICEMAN STILL HOLDS ON TO ONE LAST SECRET.

The artists' model reflects the ruggedness of the Iceman in life and likely wear and tear on his mid- to late-40s body. Despite their efforts, the scientists failed to penetrate his mummified flesh far enough to reveal the final clue to the mystery of his death: the arrowhead that killed him.

BOUNDLESS

AMERICA'S WILD AND SCENIC RIVERS

More than four decades after it became law,
a little-known federal act safeguards hundreds
of primordial waterways.

MERCED RIVER
Yosemite National Park, California

114.5 miles protected since 1987;
8 additional miles since 1992

TINAYGUK RIVER
Gates of the Arctic National Park
and Preserve, Alaska

44 miles protected since 1980

136

OWYHEE RIVER
Owyhee River Wilderness, Idaho

*120 miles protected in Oregon since
1984 and 67.2 more since 1988; 171.1
miles protected in Idaho since 2009*

AERIAL SUPPORT BY LIGHTHAWK

CHATTOOGA RIVER
Sumter National Forest, South Carolina

58.7 miles protected in North Carolina,
South Carolina, and Georgia since 1974

BY JOEL K. BOURNE, JR.
PHOTOGRAPHS BY MICHAEL MELFORD

The Middle Fork of the Salmon is not so much a river as an exuberant expression of water at play. It tumbles and turns and trips over itself for a hundred miles through the largest unbroken wilderness in the lower 48, the 2.3-million-acre Frank Church–River of No Return Wilderness, named for the pristine Salmon River gorge and the Idaho senator who made sure most of its vast watershed would stay that way. No dams temper its flow. No roads line its banks. It dances down its canyon much as it has since the glaciers receded 10,000 years ago—in spring as a raging, tree-felling torrent, in late summer as a spare, crystalline rivulet.

Today it is one of the ultimate white-water experiences in the United States, drawing thousands of visitors each year. But 60 years ago its future—and that of hundreds of other rivers across the country—looked very different. For much of the 20th century, the federal government seemed determined to dam virtually all the major rivers in the country, harnessing their power for electricity, irrigation, navigation, water supply, and flood control. The dam binge was particularly acute in the arid West, where even the Grand Canyon was slated for flooding. The Army Corps of Engineers evaluated five prospective dam sites on the Middle Fork alone. The river would have morphed into a chain of man-made lakes if two brothers hadn't helped stem the tide of concrete.

John Craighead, now 95, is legendary in the field of wildlife biology, famous with his twin brother, the late Frank Craighead, for pioneering studies of grizzly bears in Yellowstone National Park and for numerous articles and documentaries published by National Geographic. Their groundbreaking work inspired efforts to save the species from extinction in the lower 48. Yet the proudest achievement of John Craighead's long and storied life, he says, is the passage of the Wild and Scenic Rivers Act.

It took a decade of reports, lectures, and political wrangling, but when President Lyndon Johnson signed the Wild and Scenic Rivers Act in 1968, much of its language came from the Craigheads. The initial act spared eight rivers and narrow buffer zones around them from dams and development. Today the list has grown to more than 200 rivers in 39 states and Puerto Rico.

Oregon's Rogue River is one of the original eight rivers that were protected from dams in 1968.

Craighead's memory fades in and out these days, but if you ask him which river inspired him most, his answer is quick and clear: the Middle Fork of the Salmon. My son, Sam, and I were headed there, but we'd stopped to visit Craighead at his Missoula, Montana, home on our way out to paddle that river. Before we left, Craighead gave Sam a dozen spider imitations tied just for the Middle Fork's native cutthroat trout. "You know, you can't buy that fly in a store," he said, as he shook Sam's hand and gave him a knowing smile.

IT TOOK TWO ATTEMPTS before our backcountry pilot could penetrate the fog nestled in the deep valleys of the Frank Church, whose endless ridges bearded with whitebark pine keep the modern world at bay. But by midday our party of 20 was gathered by the roaring river to listen to Diana Yupe, a Shoshone-Bannock archaeologist, tell us about her people. The Sheep Eaters lived in the river corridor for thousands of years before the U.S. Cavalry drove them out. She asked us to respect the old campsites that occupy nearly every river terrace, as well as the many pictographs, including child-size red handprints, that adorn the canyon walls. Then she sent us off with a Shoshone blessing for safe travel on the river and a safe journey through life.

The day was raw and gray, the big, dry rafts inviting. Sam nonetheless picked a pair of

Joel K. Bourne, Jr., covered the Gulf of Mexico oil spill in the October 2010 issue. Michael Melford has been shooting for the magazine since 2003.

WASHINGTON

OREGON

MONTANA

IDAHO

WYOMING

SO
DAK

NEBRASKA

UTAH

CALIFORNIA

COLORADO

ARIZONA

NEW MEXICO

TEXAS

ALASKA
(Not to scale)

HAWAII

PUERTO RICO

146

MINNESOTA

WISCONSIN

MICHIGAN

MAINE

NEW HAMPSHIRE

MASSACHUSETTS

NEW YORK

CONNECTICUT

PENNSYLVANIA

NEW JERSEY

OHIO

DELAWARE

ILLINOIS

WEST VIRGINIA

MISSOURI

KENTUCKY

NORTH CAROLINA

TENNESSEE

SOUTH CAROLINA

ARKANSAS

GEORGIA

MISSISSIPPI

ALABAMA

LOUISIANA

FLORIDA

— WILD AND SCENIC RIVER SYSTEM

0 mi   200

0 km   200

PROTECTED WATERWAYS

"An unspoiled river is a very rare thing in this nation today," said President
Lyndon Johnson as he signed the Wild and Scenic Rivers Act in 1968, effectively
ending the dambuilding era of the 20th century. About 200 free-flowing rivers
(in red) are now protected by the law—a mere 0.35 percent of all U.S. river miles.

WILLIAM E. McNULTY, NGM STAFF. SOURCES: HYDROSHEDS DATABASE, WWF (RIVERS); WILD AND SCENIC RIVERS COUNCIL (DESIGNATED RIVERS)

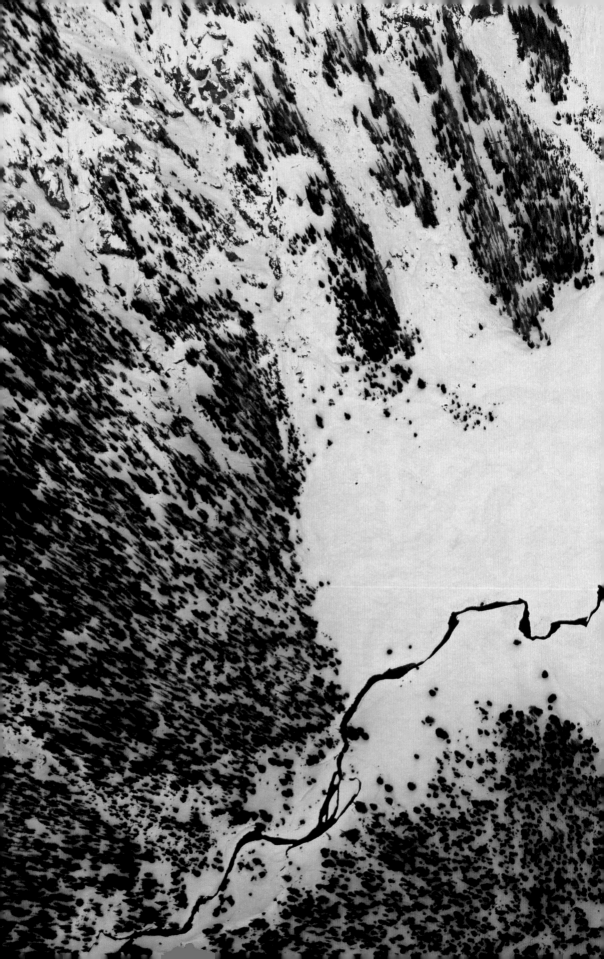

SNAKE RIVER HEADWATERS
Bridger-Teton National Forest, Wyoming

387.5 miles protected since 2009

AERIAL SUPPORT BY LIGHTHAWK

inflatable kayaks, because nothing makes you feel more 11 than bouncing down a river in an oversize inner tube. He'd never been in white water before, and he soon discovered that paddling the little kayaks, called duckies, was hard work. We struggled with headwinds, grounded on rocks, and paddled hard to keep up with the rafts. Yet tired as we were, Sam came off the river almost skipping.

That night the Milky Way choked the sky, and we couldn't find the Big Dipper in the twinkling throng. Sam turned in early, so I went down to the water to listen to the river's simple symphony. Something splashed at my feet, and when I flicked on my headlamp, I beheld a tiny fish darting around the shallows: a native chinook salmon, offspring of the big shadows we'd seen lurking in the deeper pools. Chinook fed the Sheep Eaters for millennia. Once tens of thousands of them came to spawn annually in the Middle Fork; now, eight major dams on the Snake and Columbia Rivers have exacted a toll on the fish in their 900-mile journey to the sea—one of the greatest migrations in nature.

A WILD AND SCENIC RIVER designation is no guarantee that a river will remain truly wild. In fact, several of the nation's most cherished waterways have landed on the annual Most Endangered Rivers list produced by the advocacy group American Rivers. They include southern Oregon's Chetco, where gold miners plan to suction-dredge some of the best salmon spawning grounds in the state. Maine's legendary Allagash, the river that taught Henry David Thoreau the meaning of wilderness, has long been mired in controversy over bridges and additional access points in its protected corridor. And former Vice President Walter Mondale, a co-sponsor of the Wild and Scenic Rivers Act, says of the treasured St. Croix, which runs by his Minnesota summer home: "If this river is ever destroyed, it'll die of nicks and cuts. A bridge here, a power line there. These threats are everywhere," he adds, "and they have to be fought everywhere. Just go to one of the unprotected rivers in the Northeast or South and see how polluted they are."

The stream of my youth, North Carolina's aptly named Tar, is one such river, though my friends and I were too young to know the difference then. We caught bass and bluegills

IT WAS A LIVING PAGE FROM AMERICA'S PAST, WHEN EVERY RIVER WAS CLEAN, POTABLE, AND FULL OF LIFE.

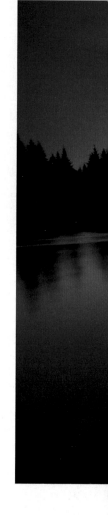

from beneath the rafts of old soda and bleach bottles that floated at each logjam. We shot the ducks that exploded from the quiet bends where discarded washing machines and tires lay. We waded when the water dropped to knee-deep in summer and carried a faint whiff of the sewage treatment plant upstream. Though I caught countless fish from the Tar's waters, I released them to their turbid home. My parents drew the line at eating them.

Such threats seemed many miles and moons from the clear, clean water of central Idaho. The next day the sun rose white-hot above the ridgeline, turning the Middle Fork into an undulating strand of emeralds. A herd of bighorn sheep joined us for breakfast. Bald and golden eagles glared at us from their perches as American dippers flitted from rock to rock. The guides filled

Moonlight bathes a birchbark canoe on Maine's Allagash Wilderness Waterway, a tranquil spot for paddlers.

our water jugs from springs we passed while the anglers among us hooked hungry trout on what seemed like every other cast. It was a living page from America's past, when every river was clean, potable, and full of life.

After lunch on a gravel bar I sat in the shade and watched Sam struggle with the fly rod as most beginners do, flailing it like a whip instead of achieving that "art...performed on a four-count rhythm between ten and two o'clock," as Norman Maclean wrote in *A River Runs Through It*. But gradually he checked himself and stopped the rod close to ten. The line uncurled on the water like a prayer, dropping the Craighead spider fly into an alluring eddy. He was too pleased with himself to notice the shimmering torpedo emerge from the depths. Only when he tried to back-cast did he find himself hooked into a living, breathing dynamo. This was no video game, no virtual walleye of Wii. This was bare-foot boy against bantamweight pisces, and the age-old fight was on. As the two splashed in the cool, green water, whoops rose from the bank. The bronze bomber skittered onto shore, the same westslope cutthroat with its jaunty red sash that so delighted Lewis and Clark.

Sam was beaming, caught deep in Craighead's web. I once asked Craighead why wild rivers were such a crucial issue for him, thinking he would wax philosophical about the need for wild things in an increasingly man-made world. He shrugged. "I just loved rivers," he said.

It was enough. Because he and others loved moving, living, untarnished waters, we now have some left to cherish. To help us think more like a river, less like a dam. □

MIDDLE FORK
OF THE SALMON RIVER
Salmon-Challis National Forest, Idaho

104 miles protected since 1968

ALLAGASH RIVER
Aroostook County, Maine

92.5 miles protected since 1970

TLIKAKILA RIVER
Lake Clark National Park and Preserve, Alaska

51 miles protected since 1980

NG CONNECT

Every month this page features our staff picks of National Geographic Society products and events. For more go to *nglive/events.org*.

MOVIE

Flying Monsters 3D

Soar with pterosaurs as David Attenborough takes you back millions of years, to a world where reptiles with 40-foot wingspans ruled the skies. Computer-generated imagery (CGI) and 3-D technology bring these beasts to life, as Attenborough reveals how and why they flew. In theaters now.

LECTURE

ON THE TRAIL OF THE TIGER For next month's feature story on tigers, wildlife photographer Steve Winter traveled to India, Indonesia, and Thailand. Hear his tales of pursuing the world's largest cats and see the stunning images at National Geographic headquarters in Washington, D.C., on November 30. Visit *nglive.org* for tickets.

EXHIBIT

GOLD HOARD The Anglo-Saxon gold hoard is coming to Washington, D.C. View more than a hundred artifacts, including intricate sword-hilt rings (left). At the National Geographic Museum until March 4. Go to *ngmuseum.org* and enter "NGMAG" for discounted admission.

APP

WORLD ATLAS BY NATIONAL GEOGRAPHIC Hold the world in your hand with this interactive app featuring a 3-D globe and our database of facts and flags. In the App Store ($1.99).

BOOK

LOST GOLD OF THE DARK AGES Dig deeper into the mystery of England's buried Anglo-Saxon gold. This book illuminates an era of myth and legend with photos and in-depth analysis of the amazing discovery featured on this issue's cover. Available now ($35).

Free Download of the Month

Blue King Brown *Worldwize*

Australian band Blue King Brown channels a world of influences into its propulsive sound. Santana-like Latin percussion, the reggae wisdom of Bob Marley, and the anticolonial populism of Fela Kuti all echo through the band's unique take on roots-rock-reggae. Download a free song from its latest album, *Worldwize*, at *natgeomusic.net/free*.

Rest for the Weary

Since 2008 Erika Larsen has been living in Norway's extreme northeast with a family of Sami reindeer herders. In addition to photographing their way of life, she works keeping house for them. This immersion, she says, helps her better understand the culture, which can be tough but is not without flashes of tenderness. That warmth is exemplified in this image of a tired young reindeer getting a lift instead of having to walk. "With the Sami herders," she says, "I've observed nature being at once beautiful and brutal." —*Catherine Zuckerman*

BEHIND THE LENS

Why is this reindeer lashed to a sled?

EL: I took this in May, when we were moving the reindeer north from Kautokeino toward the sea. It's an 80-mile trip, and this calf was struggling to keep up. So a herder placed it on a sled, tying it down to hold it secure. Then he hitched the sled to his snowmobile and pulled the reindeer along.

What about this scene do you find compelling?

This was the first time I had witnessed the practice of carrying reindeer. The herders do this so the calves don't overexert themselves and end up dying. I felt that it was important to show this side of things, this compassion. Of course the herders don't want the calf to die—it represents food and money. But they also don't want it to suffer while it's alive. The herders are not overly sensitive, but to the degree that one can care for a wild animal, they do. It's not easy to put into words. That's probably why I took a picture instead.

Pearl Strivers

A car's old gas tank and some garden hose compose a homemade helmet for this Mississippi River pearl diver. Notes with the photo claim the apparatus enabled the man to "go down 70 feet, and remain down one and a half hours."

He would have needed that much time to find anything. When this photo was taken in 1938, the Mississippi's population of pearly mussels had already been largely depleted for use by button factories. For them, the mussels' shells proved more valuable than the gem sometimes inside. One bivalve could yield 24 buttons punched from its halves—and some six billion buttons were produced in the U.S. in 1916 alone. Though most pearl-button factories did not survive the 1940s rage for plastic buttons (not to mention zippers), the end of the harvests did not bring the Mississippi's mussels numbers back. Dozens of its species are now classified as endangered or threatened. Some might say they're as rare as pearls. —Margaret G. Zackowitz

Flashback Archive Find all the photos at **ngm.com.**

NATIONAL GEOGRAPHIC (ISSN 0027-9358) PUBLISHED MONTHLY BY THE NATIONAL GEOGRAPHIC SOCIETY, 1145 17TH ST. NW, WASHINGTON, DC 20036. ONE YEAR MEMBERSHIP: $34.00 U.S. DELIVERY, $38.00 TO CANADA, $49.50 TO INTERNATIONAL ADDRESSES. SINGLE ISSUE: $7.00 U.S. DELIVERY, $10.00 CANADA, $15.00 INTERNATIONAL. (ALL PRICES IN U.S. FUNDS; INCLUDES SHIPPING AND HAN-DLING.) PERIODICALS POSTAGE PAID AT WASHINGTON, DC, AND ADDITIONAL MAILING OFFICES. POSTMASTER: SEND ADDRESS CHANGES TO NATIONAL GEOGRAPHIC, PO BOX 63002, TAMPA, FL 33663. IN CANADA, AGREEMENT NUMBER 40063649, RETURN UNDELIVERABLE ADDRESSES TO NATIONAL GEOGRAPHIC, PO BOX 4412 STN. A, TORONTO, ONTARIO M5W 3W2. UNITED KINGDOM NEWSSTAND PRICE £4.99. REPR. EN FRANCE: EMD FRANCE SA, BP 1029, 59011 LILLE CEDEX; TEL. 320.300.302; CPPAP 0710U89037; DIRECTEUR PUBLICATION: D. TASSINARI DIR. RESP. ITALY; RAPP IMD SRL, VIA G. DA VELATE 11, 20162 MILANO; AUT. TRIB. MI 258 26/5/84 POSTE ITALIANE SPA; SPED. ABB. POST. DL 353/2003 (CONV L.27/02/2004 N.46) ART 1 C. 1 DCB MILANO STAMPA QUAD/GRAPHICS, MARTINSBURG, WV 25401. MEMBERS: IF THE POSTAL SERVICE ALERTS US THAT YOUR MAGAZINE IS UNDELIVERABLE, WE HAVE NO FURTHER OBLIGATION UNLESS WE RECEIVE A CORRECTED ADDRESS WITHIN TWO YEARS.